My Favourite Person

Idols & Icons

Edited by Angela Fairbrace

First published in Great Britain in 2009 by:

 Young**Writers**

Young Writers
Remus House
Coltsfoot Drive
Peterborough
PE2 9JX
Telephone: 01733 890066
Website: www.youngwriters.co.uk

Foreword

Our 'My Favourite Person 2009' poetry competition attracted young aspiring poets to show their admiration for those who have made an impact in their life. What better way to let those closest know how much they are appreciated.

We are delighted to present 'Idols & Icons'. After reading through the hundreds of entries it is clear the amount of enthusiasm and love that went into writing these poems, therefore we hope you'll agree they are an inspiring and heart-warming read.

Young Writers was established in 1991 to promote poetry and creative writing to schoolchildren and encourage them to read, write and enjoy it. Here at Young Writers we are sure you'll agree that this special edition achieves our aim and celebrates today's wealth of young writing talent. We hope you enjoy 'Idols & Icons' for many years to come.

Contents

Thanaa Ajeigbe (11) 1
Baveena Heer (14) 2
Hadiah Shaikh (11)..............3
Kayleigh Robinson (10) 4
Jewel Hetherington (9)...........5
Jieyi Li (9)..............6
Cara Bacon (6) 7
Beatrice Lander (10)..............8
Hannah Ost (10) 9
Bethany Shannon Lepetit (11) 10
Ella Hawley (14) 11
Ayesha White (11)..............12
Amaan Anthony Broughton (6)...........13
Emma Brown (11) 14
Dylan Davidson (11) 15
Jessie Forsythe (8)..............16
Fatma Mohamed 17
Shakeel Rahman (11)..............18
Rachael Brown (9)..............19
Georgia Hardy (11)..............20
Lauren Gallacher (10) 20
Savini Hewage (11) 21
Stephanie Poon (10) 22
Oscar Saharoy (8) 23
Sami Patel (9)..............23
Briony Tripp (11)..............24
Emily Brown (6) 24
Hollie Belford (11)..............25
Bethany McNerlin (10) 25
Jemma Wolfe (11) 26
Megan Burns (11)..............26
Kate Blundel (11) 27
Georgia Talman (9)..............27
Rachel Fu (13) 28
Leah Duery (13) 28
Bethany Carter (10) 29
Aaron Dean (10)..............29
Sheldon Delices (11)..............30
Victoria Towersey (9)..............30
Isabel Black (10) 31
Daniel Phillips (9)..............31

Sophie Mill (11)..............32
Madia Rehman (10)..............32
Philippa Rose Humphreys (10)...........33
Samantha Widdas (9)..............33
Sophie Kidder (10)..............34
Ellissa Millard (11)..............35
Chelsea Stemp (10) 35
Charlotte Fisher (9)..............36
Lucas Claxton (8)..............36
Hannah Tiffany (10)..............37
Kelsey Scott (10)..............37
Lewis Green (11)..............38
Laura Dawe (9)..............38
Zainab Faruqi (10)..............39
Chelsea Gault (9)..............39
Ellie Kelly (11)..............40
Callum Loader (10)..............41
Sophie Sarney (10)..............42
Bryony Amelia Mead (11) 42
Stephanie Hall (10)..............43
Rhea Sokhi (9) 43
Amanda Masuku (11) 44
Eden O'Shea-Price (10)..............44
Tazmin Clements (10)..............45
Faye Pollard (11)..............45
Joshua Slate (11)..............46
Georgia Thorpe (11) 47
Aimee Wells (7)..............47
Emily Barrett (11)..............48
Chloe Dooley (10) 48
Rosalind Henderson (11)..............49
Ishrath Iqbal (11) 49
Hannah Ransom (10)..............50
Isabella Atherley (10) 50
Sophie Le Feuvre (9)..............51
Ophelia Morley (10)..............51
Jovarn Blair (11)..............52
Jami Harris (9)..............52
Amy Gunning (11)..............53
Chloe Lloyd (11)..............53
Maisie Butcher (11) 54

Lily Slater (6) 54
Nicola Rose (11) 55
Lydia Talman (10) 55
Rhian Bland (10)..................................56
Shalayka Shephard (10)....................56
Alida Evans (13) 57
Danielle Greengrass (11) 58
Eve Bishop (10) 58
Bethany Bristol (9)..............................59
Alexander Bojic-Aguilar (10) 59
Jacob Seelochan (11)..........................60
Elisha Wraith (9) 61
Thomas Stephens (8) 61
Angel Osei-Kissi (10)..........................62
Rhianna McCaffrey (9) 62
Keri Heddle (8)....................................63
Penelope Young (11) 63
Maizie Ferrett (10) 64
Dana Kenneally-Forrester (10)..........64
Summer Valentine (11) 65
Adam Dearsley (11).............................66
Kishan Sharma (11).............................66
Lauren Quayle (6)................................67
Daniel Nunn (9) 67
Cerys Paterson (9)..............................68
Jordan Elizabeth Ellis (11) 68
Elaine Haripersaud (8) 69
Isla Lury (9)...69
Ishraq Choudhury Tasnim (9)............70
Kelly Chowdhury (10) 70
Leah Gibby (11)..................................71
Lucy McGillivray (7)............................71
Edriene Padua (8) 72
Katie Dunning (11) 72
Megan Roberts (11) 73
Amber Wollen (9)................................73
Francesca Cavadino (8)......................74
Matthew Brooks (11)...........................74
Lola Francis (10) 75
Anna Wernick (12)..............................75
Rochelle Devonport (10) 76
Abigail Markwick (13) 76
Freya Ireland (11) 77
Luke Fowler (6)...................................77
Robyn Gunn (11).................................78

Nekeshia McKenzie (11) 78
Liberty Lee (9).....................................79
Bethany Jayne May Stannard (10) 79
Suzanna Cavadino (6)........................80
Holly Vipond (10)................................80
Brae Parker (9)....................................81
Farzana Akhtar (10) 81
Eden Byrne-Young (11) 82
Georgia Clarke (11).............................82
Nuha Chowdhury (10) 83
Stephanie Joy Evans (11)...................83
Georgia Bartram (11) 84
Liam Meah (9) 84
Bayan Fadlalla (10) 85
Sonnie Smith (11) 85
Leah Leonardi (10)..............................86
Jennifer Stokes (10)...........................86
Maddie Morris (10)..............................87
Abbey Bedford (11) 87
Janine Brown (11)...............................88
Amber Percival (11).............................88
Rachel Eager (11) 89
Amine Nur Dincer (11).........................89
Shaquille Stephens (11).....................90
Sulaiman Faruqi (8) 90
Laura Dunleavy (11) 91
Tanya Gupta Telukunta (9).................91
Millie Chappell (10)............................92
Dearbhail McCaffrey (11)...................92
Emma Scott (11) 93
Chase-Lee De'Ath (9) 93
Timothy MacKenzie (11).....................94
Chloe Campbell (10)...........................94
Roshni Makwana (12)..........................95
Iqra Ahmed (12) 95
Rebecca Smith (12).............................96
Yasmin Boyall (10)..............................96
Louise Oldham (11) 97
Belinda Carini-Nunn (10) 97
Ibrahim Sheikh (11) 98
Mark Facey (11) 98
Jack Lane (11) 99
Emily Sheppard (10)...........................99
Jordon Anderson (8).........................100
Elizabeth Hitchcock (12)..................100

Bethany Nash (10) 101
Laura Hutchinson (11)......................101
Henna Pratik Patel (11) 102
Sruti Saraswatula (8).......................102
Nieve Walton-O'Brien (10)...............103
Eddy Oliveira (10)............................103
Shauna Green (11) 104
Leigh-Anne Preston (11) 104
Amy Young (11)...............................105
Emily Maloney (6)............................105
Jaidyn Dilon Murray (10) 106
Brogan Pickering (11) 106
Nazifa Ibrahim (11) 107
Tony Colvin (10)...............................107
Finnlay Walsh (10)...........................108
Marc Piper (11) 108
Sophie Goodenough (10)..................109
Lucy Mackintosh (11).......................109
Natasha Smith (9) 110
Sidra Zainab (10) 110
Larissa Aravantinou (10)..................111
Kaitlyn Templeman (10)....................111
Nora Berzina (10) 112
Elizabeth Drinkwater (10) 112
Reshmi Jay Patel (10) 113
Hannah Berry (11)...........................113
Alexander Wellington (10)................114
Hetty Bostock (10)...........................114
Francesca Riley (10) 115
Junaid Saddique (9) 115
Kelsey Brigden (11)..........................116
Bayse Genc (10)...............................116
Reece Boulton (10) 117
Danielle Jones (11) 117
Hannah Greenwood (9).....................118
Emily Longhurst (8) 118
Katherine Fallows (10) 119
Harrison Mills (9) 119
Hannah Moore (8) 120
Guanhong Li (11).............................120
Bethany Marshall (11)......................121
Simran Seehra (11) 121
Emily-Frances Allen (11) 122
Herjyot Manku (10) 122
Carla Nevin (8) 123

Katie Knowles (11)...........................123
Heather Wickens (11) 124
Emma Davey (12) 124
Antonia Day (11) 125
Isabelle Jackson (10).......................125
Hannah Gowen (9) 126
Emma Howes (9) 126
Lauren Grattage (11) 127
Bethany-Mae Jones (10) 127
George Lucas (13)............................128
Kayleigh Corbet-Adams (11) 128
Cerys McGivern (11).........................129
Lauryn Douglas Hayward (11) 129
Stuart Boyce (12).............................130
Sonia Puri (11) 130
Dana Leslie (11)..............................131
Tolia Uwalaka (10) 131
Elena Napoliello (9)..........................132
Caroline Richardson (10) 132
Chelsea Williams (11) 133
Joana Carvalho 133
Hamza Khan (9)...............................134
Safia Mahmood (8)...........................134
Jordan Eyre (10)..............................135
Ellie McIntyre (11)............................135
Harley Jones (10) 136
Krista Armstrong (13) 136
Aoife Cassidy (10)............................137
Lucy Reeve (8) 137
Emma Danielle Claxton (11)............138
Florence Howard (11)........................138
Alex Moreland (11)...........................139
Emily Denny (11) 139
Alana Stevenson (10).......................140
Laurie Reznik (10)............................140
Charley Hodges (10) 141
Bethany Wilson (9)...........................141
Libby Spokes (10) 142
Chloe Mead (9)................................142
Holly Riglar (15) 143
Maryam Shafiq (10)..........................143
Hanisha Kaur (12) 144
Brittany Buttle (10) 144
Saffron-Alicia Best (9) 145
Jake Coombs (10)............................145

Rebekah Smith (10) 146
Sammy Fowler (9).............................146
Jessica Apps (10) 147
Emily Millard (9) 147
Danielle Thornborough (11)..............148
Emily Cribb (10)...............................148
Georgia Middleton (10) 149
Luana Ebiogwu (11).........................149
Natalie Warner (11).........................150
Yassmine Akesbi (11) 150
Madeeha Anam Rafique (12)...........151
Panashe Danga (9)..........................151
Rebecca Cliffe (11) 152
Phoebe Nickolls (8) 152
Megan Chadwick (9) 153
Thomas Evans (10) 153
Meredith Webb (10) 154
Katie Greenaway (11)......................154
Caitlin Hinds (8) 155
Charis Fage (10)..............................155
Shannon Drew (12)..........................155
Liam Griffiths (6)..............................156
Troy Crombie (12)............................156
Lewis Hunter (8)..............................156
Lena Jones (10)...............................157
Alicia Reid (11)................................157
Kes Sinfield (10) 157
Lancy Miranda (14) 158
Jaymie Wright (10) 158
Lisa-Marie Curley (8).......................158
Georgia Watts (9)............................159
Indiana Fofie-Collins (9)...................159
Joanna Poole (11) 159
Harry Siderfin (9) 160
Siobhan Lock (10) 160
Jamielee Zwart (10) 160
Chloë Ball (8) 161
Henry Dearn.....................................161
Kayley Sharp (11)............................161
Sarah Warner (10)...........................162
Georgia Howard (9) 162
Kirstie Goodchild (9) 162
Amy Ingram (9)................................163
Aston Crombie (10) 163
Harvey Bolton (9) 163

Chanttel Wright (10).........................164
Amy Crain (11) 164
Gurneet Brar (10)............................164
Beth Egan (12) 165
Mustafa Elsherkisi (11)....................165
Jade Viccars (10) 165
Nabeeda Bakali (13) 166
Rebecca Jeffery (8).........................166
Jessica Francis (10) 166
Aaliyah Chileshe (11) 167
Arron Drummond (8).........................167
Charlotte Hamilton (11) 167
Samuel Lewis Lunn (8) 168
Tiaylor-Marie Davis (8).....................168
Charlotte Cooper (9) 168
Lauren Emily Cadge (12)..................169
Bethani Partridge (11) 169
Sam Cooper (9) 169
Erin Fyfe-McWilliam (11) 170
Emily Moore (10)..............................170
Jordan Drummond (6) 170
Ben Morgan (9) 171
Cameron Cook (10) 171
Hannah Furness (9)..........................171
Caryn Pearce (11) 172
Sam Harvey (10) 172
Jade Poyser (8) 172
Eleanor Shanahan (10).....................173
Alicia Ross (6)..................................173

The Poems

You!

You magnify my happiness
When I am feeling glad;
You help to heal my injured heart
Whenever I am sad.
You've been there for me
Through the good times and the bad,
I know I can count on you
To be there when I'm mad.

Life without you
Just wouldn't be right.
I wouldn't be able to get through
Each day and night.

When I've had a bad day
I know that you're only a call away.
When life takes that crazy turn
You are always there to help me learn.

We've had so many good times together,
I know we'll be best friends forever.
No matter where we are
I know we'll never be too far.

You're my idol, my sister, my friend,
We'll be together till the end.
Even when we're old and grey,
You'll be here still,
To help me get on my way.

You're such a pleasure in my life;
I hope that you can see
How meaningful your friendship is,
You're a total joy to me.

You are my favourite person
On this entire Earth,
You're the person who has helped me through
All the way since childbirth.

Thanaa Ajeigbe (11)

My Favourite Person

When I was young,
Through the blades of green grass and under the gooseberry groves,
Around the dense thickets that surrounded us, we strolled.
Past the blossoming meadows abundant in daffodils,
Past the prairie lying below the dusty pink of the sinking sun,
Past the galloping horses that whinnied, we rolled.

We would grasp our brolly securely and zip up to the neck,
As we heard the drum beat and the relentless pattering of rain.
Dressed in our glossy red wellingtons and bright blue anoraks,
As we trod on the pools of puddles,
With a beaming smile printed on our faces,
We skipped heartily down the lane.

You comforted me while I stayed awake,
Apprehensive, vexed, petrified, not asleep but
Lying rigidly like a frozen pea on my bed,
Trying to shut out those dreaded nightmares of ghoulish trickery,
Trying to fasten a lock on a bolted chest in the corner of my head.
My eyes were open wide as I was frightened
Of what might be lurking outside;
Outside the warmth of my blanket, beyond our
Concealed burrow of faith.
Luckily you were always by my side,
Whom I could consult when I was troubled,
The only one who I could confide.

On Wednesdays we cherished our moment, sitting on our bottoms,
Hands placed on our laps, lips tightly closed,
By Mrs Hammond during reading time.
As she played the part of the Mad Hatter,
I starred as Alice and you had no role
So attempted to sing along with the riddled rhyme.
Not noting that I was prancing around in a plain white overall,
Acting like a baffled fool, noticing that you resembled one too.

During maths we concentrated counting to twenty and back,
In fits of laughter till our sides were in stitches due to larking about,
Wondering how on earth we would find signs
For the path to solve our problem,
'Oh bother me,' our fingers were running out!

You and me, Nathalie and Buttons, together at school,
Four equals two and two!

I clung onto you tight by your stuffed hand
With all the might I could muster,
Willing to put up a merciless fight,
Not keen on releasing my fixed grip and parting
With the countless memories that we had made:
The endless games we had played
The friendship that yet remained
The secrets we had exchanged
The thoughts we had shared
The many years I had cared
For you when I was oblivious and unknowing,
Unaware that the tick-tock of the time had been gradually slowing -
But now I opened my eyes and could clearly see
That the treasured possession
With two bowed plaits of woollen hair lying before me,
Was a rag doll.

Baveena Heer (14)

A Friend . . .

Someone to keep,
Someone to love,
With a shoulder to cry on,
Like a beautiful white dove.

Rest your head with happiness
On my bright side,
That glows just for you,
With mighty pride.

You are precious to me,
You're sweet and nice,
And you can't imagine it,
And it's worth no price.

Remember this, we are good friends,
Which we do not take for granted.

Hadiah Shaikh (11)

My Family

Dad
I have a fantastic dad
He's the barbecue king
He's the best at everything
He takes us on the best holidays
And we have loads of fun
But most of all
His cuddles are number one.

Mum
She works really hard every day
To keep us happy in every way
Washing our clothes, cooking our tea
Baking the tastiest cakes just for me
And she always has a good laugh
While giving me a bath
What a busy bee!

Dylan
He is my baby brother
Like no other
Small and sweet
You could always give him a treat
Then he would smile and giggle
Put on the music and watch him wiggle!

Mary
My little sister Mary
Is like a little fairy
Always an angel
Helping us all
Even though she isn't that tall
But she's loads of fun
When we play in the bright round sun.

Jamie
Jamie is my big brother
He is active and really fun
His cooking is almost as good as Mum's.

Oliver

He is a little devil
Cheeky as can be
Playing with sand and Lego
And he always plays with me
My little brother Oliver
He is my star by far
Crunching on his favourite chocolate bar.

Family
That's my family
They are all my favourite
I couldn't choose
I wanted to write about them all
Even if I'd lose!

Kayleigh Robinson (10)

My Godfather

My favourite person, his name is John.
He's full of laughter and so much fun!
He picks me up from school one day a week,
He always brings me a special treat.
Chocolate, crisps and fizzy pop,
I must admit I scoff the lot!

He loves shows like 'Countdown' and 'The Weakest Link'
He shouts out all the answers before I can think!
Sometimes, when we wait for dinner to cook
I'll be the teacher and make John read a book!

At draughts and card games I always win
'She is the champ,' says John with a grin.
When it is sunny we go to the park,
John will push me on the swing
Until nearly dark.

When I grow up and leave home,
I know we will always be talking on the phone.
He will always be my godfather and favourite person too,
Because without John, my life would be poo!

Jewel Hetherington (9)

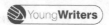

Never, But Forever

When I was in the shadows
With heavy crying clouds over me
Did anyone come?

When I was down
And oh, my soul so weary
Did anyone help comfort me?

When I was lonely
With sadness creeping up my soul
Did anyone share it with me?

When I was unfortunate
With no hope left
Did anyone come up with a solution to help?

When I was afraid
With ice-cold blood and a fear-struck heart
Did anyone come and say everything would be alright?

When I was gobsmacked
Shocked to see the secrets and lies
Did anyone tell me that the future would be full of joy?

No one, nobody, no one cared
Which left me in the darkness . . .

But you, you came
You helped me
You did what you could

You comforted me
You shared with me
You had a solution to help

You told me things would be alright
You told me the future would be full of joy
Thank you

You cared
You noticed
You knew how it felt

It's too bad that you're gone
From then, no other friend mattered to me

I'll never forget you
As long as I live
Until I die

I'll call you when I can
I'd tell you my every secret
I'll be happy to see you again

Loads of times you helped me
And I'll never forget those moments
Time will never whisk you away
Tomorrow and on
I'll always think of your name
Again and again.

Jieyi Li (9)

My Favourite Person

My granda is my favourite person in the world.
He takes me shopping when he is not working hard.

He buys me shoes and clothes and loves to act the clown
And makes me smile when I am feeling down.

When he is sleeping he snores a lot
But if I tell him he says he does not.

No matter what, I love him so
And I do not like it when he has to go.

Cara Bacon (6)

My Friend In My Dreams

There once lived a boy, but he was not an ordinary child . . .

Sam was a young boy about 10 years old,
He was courageous, daring, confident and bold.
His hair was as dark as the dead of night,
His eyes were ebony-black, lit up by one single light.
His mouth was a curve of cheekiness,
His face always beamed with happiness . . .

When he was orphaned his happiness turned into dust,
He thought, *I will do anything that I must.*
Soon Sam had new parents and a new life.
He had a stingy mean father and his boastful wife.
Sam soon realised he must be free,
He climbed out the window and into the sea.

He dived down and down into the deep blue water,
Expecting never to be seen ever after.
His parents soon discovered he was on the go,
He was their responsibility so they searched high and low.
Soon they found him in the depths of the sea,
Sam was clutching, very tightly, to a key.

His parents watched silently, not uttering a word
But soon to Sam and his parents it occurred . . .
The key was the answer to a small trapdoor,
The door was found upon the sea floor.
Sam searched long and hard
Until he found a glittering card.

The card told him where to look,
It told him to look for a golden hook.
In no time Sam found a wooden door
Meanwhile his parents were full of bore.
He slowly unlocked the door and found a passageway,
As he was swimming he thought this was his best day.

Sam's parents had followed him through,
As they neared him he shouted, 'Who are you?'
Sam instantly knew it was his horrid parents,
He suddenly wished, in-between them, was a fence.
Sam quickly swam up to the small door,

He badly wanted to discover more.

He locked his bad-tempered parents in,
He thought it was better than throwing them in the bin!
Sam speedily buried the golden key.
He was a clever boy wasn't he!

After getting out of the water
He realised he'd never see his parents ever after.
That evening when he was thinking about the key
He realised that he could breathe under the sea!

Something in that boy is very mysterious
And no one will know what it is . . .

Beatrice Lander (10)

My Favourite People Are . . .

My favourite people are my family,
I really can't decide who means more to me.
They help me when I'm troubled,
They love and cuddle me,
I'd never ever leave them because they belong to me.

My favourite people are my family,
I really can't decide who means more to me.
They give me confidence,
They boost me on the way,
They wave me from the gate as I enter school that day.

My favourite people are my family,
I really can't decide who means more to me.
They keep me fit and healthy,
They care for me all day,
They'll never ever leave me, or ever go away.

My favourite people are my family,
I really can't decide who means more to me.
My sister means the world to me,
So do my mum and dad,
They are the best family that I could ever dream to have.

Hannah Ost (10)

My Mum

My favourite person
Is my mum
Who changed my nappy
And wiped my bum

My mum was there
Every step of the way
Watching me and watching me
Day by day

She brushed my hair
And changed my clothes
She said to me yesterday
I love you loads

She took me to school
And said bye-bye
Gave me some dinner
Then said, 'Night, night.'

She brushed my teeth
And gave me baths
Took me to the park
And we had loads of laughs

She's very pretty
But very small
Unlike me, Beth
I'm very tall

I love you mum
She loves me too
I hope so
I'm sure it's true

She wears blue socks
She wears boyish clothes
She loves to play games
Has no time to doze.

Bethany Shannon Lepetit (11)

The Lamp Of Life

The start of the tale,
Goes something like this,
I'm inspired by heroes,
Let me reminisce.

The water was cold and the tide was in,
She asked herself, *How did I sin?*
She was struggling now; it was far too deep,
She screamed for help,
But still no peep.

She asked the good ord, why o why,
How to face death eye to eye,
She felt hopeless now, completely afraid
And wished for a person to come to her aid.

She blinked three times and saw something bright,
A very gentle, peaceful light,
Then a voice around her,
Told her not to panic,
It was not calm but not manic,
She turned to see a figure on the seaside, so foggy and damp,
This was her saviour with the lamp.

On a bicycle, in a red truck, in a car or on foot,
These are the saviours of the modern day world,
They all fit in the lessons we learn,
Like a police officer, a fireman, a nurse or a doctor,
They pass on, forgotten in time,
And I'll say it only once, so I can make my point,
Listen! This moment is mine,
I have not met my favourite person,
But I know of the heroes they are,
They can be calm but not manic,
They are peace makers and help with panic,
These are the people in the situations, so foggy and damp,
These are the people who carry a lamp.

Ella Hawley (14)

My Mum!

My mum is always there
to catch me when I fall.

My mum helps me all she can,
she resolves it all.

My mum is there to guide me,
homework, friends and boys!

My mum has been like me herself,
she knows all the tricks and ploys!

My mum would never let me down,
for her I would do the same.

My mum is loving and special,
my happiness is her aim.

My mum is clever and beautiful,
I hope I'm like her one day!

My mum is hardworking and caring,
she is behind me all the way.

My mum does so much for me,
always with a gorgeous smile.

My mum shouts and yells sometimes,
it only lasts a while!

My mum can be strict about the rules,
it's all for my own good.

My mum makes sure that I behave,
always doing as I should.

My mum is kind and loyal,
the best friend I could choose.

My mum is the best there is,
together we cannot lose!

Ayesha White (11)

Liverpool Football Club

'I love Liverpool!'
One day we went to a football match
It was Liverpool vs Arsenal
Torres scored two and Benayoun two
It was 4 all not 4 nil.

'I love Liverpool!'
Arshavin scored all four for Arsenal
The match was at Anfield, that's Liverpool's ground
I know that because Liverpool were in red
And Arsenal were in yellow.

'I love Liverpool!'
Gerrard didn't score that day
But it didn't matter
The crowd were screaming really loud
Even us, we were yelling and laughing.

'I love Liverpool!'
We were shouting at the ref!
Benitez was looking unhappy
Like he always does
Thank you fans out there!

'I love Liverpool!'
Who loves Liverpool Football Club?
I'm not from Liverpool
I'm from Preston
But that doesn't matter.

'I love Liverpool!'
Liverpool FC rules!
They are really cool
They are very good at football
See you later fans out there!

Amaan Anthony Broughton (6)

My Little Nan

Her silvery, grey, curly hair,
The Pinocchio pin she bought, that I pinned to my bear.
Her pale face was neither hot nor cold,
She was still young and not at all old.
She always laughed and was always very funny,
And was generous with her pocket money.
She always gave lovely big hugs and kisses,
And whenever she came for tea she'd tell Mum she'd do the dishes.
She had a lot of sayings and one was 'don't you dare'.
When my brother and I argued, she'd always make it fair.
The doll of the Spanish dancer that she gave to me,
And the way she was never frightened by any size bee.
Turkish delight was one of her favourite treats.
Though she never ate too many sweets.
Pepe, the budgie, her little blue friend,
The Scottish Westie postcard that we wanted to send.
As I was getting taller, she was getting small,
Although many times she had walked along Chester's wall.
She loved chips with vinegar, which had to be malt,
And the Disney films we watched together, created by Mr Walt.
Her long back garden with all the plants and trees,
When at her front door she got mixed up with her keys.
The Christmas collar she bought for Hamish the dog,
She loved the pond, which usually held a frog.
She had these long, fluffy snakes,
And lovely rich tea finger biscuits and yummy cakes.
Her loving, sweet, bouncy laugh,
She loved Ormskirk Park, where we took the rounded path.
Even though we can no longer see her,
We know she's always near.
We love her in every way,
Forever and a day.

Emma Brown (11)

My Favourite Person

My favourite person is my mum
Man, she is so very fun
Some people may think she's mad
But she's my mum and I am glad

She works her socks off every day
Giving our rabbits loads of hay
She does the cooking and washes the dishes
Well, she's granted all my wishes

She's doing a run for Cancer Research UK
It makes me want to shout, *'Hooray!'*
She's been out practising every week
I'm sure her photo's on the Internet
Why not have a peek?

She's the greatest mum I could ever dream
I wouldn't swap her for ice cream
Her hugs are so very delightful
She gives me them when I feel frightful

I'm proud to have her as a mum
She does things with me when I want to have fun
If mums were stars, she would shine over all
She's loved me since before I could crawl

Her eyes are blue, her hair is brown
She is always smiling, there's never a frown
When I fall over, she picks me up
When I play football, she wishes me good luck

This is the end of the story of my mum
I hope when listening, you had fun
Some people may think she's mad
But she's my mum and I am glad.

Dylan Davidson (11)

My Favourite People

My favourite person is my mum.
She is kind and very helpful!

M y mum is lovely
U nderstanding is what she does to me
M y, I love her
M ummy I call her really
Y ummy dinners she cooks.

My other favourite people are my grandparents!
They are very kind!

G ranny and Grandpa
R eally kind
A lways loving
N ever cross
D eafening fun
P layful days
A nd I love them so much
R aving fun and raving days
E very day I love them
N anny and Grandad
T all day, short day, every day
S o I love them.

My favourite people are my family!

F amily are the best
A im high that's what we do
M y family are the greatest
I love them all
L ove my family
Y ou, me, family.

Love them.

Jessie Forsythe (8)

Caring Mum

My favourite person is my mum
She cares for me every way
Whenever I'm in a bad mood
She always knows what to say

She always makes me dinner
She always makes lunch
If I'm hungry
She'll give me something to *crunch!*

My beautiful, caring mum
Is as kind as Cinderella
Whenever it's raining
She always has an umbrella

She is as bright as that shining sun
And is always filled with fun
You can say she's very joyful
And she's never mad like a bull

We all know we have our mums
Even if you're not together
She's still out there caring
For your whole life and forever

My favourite person is my mum
She cares for me every way
Whenever I'm in a bad mood
She always knows what to say

She always makes me dinner
She always makes me lunch
If I'm hungry
She'll give me something to *crunch!*

Fatma Mohamed

Mr Magnanimous Or Mr M For Short

My favourite person
Or Mr M for short
Was my Year Six teacher
And to me he taught

Maths, English, science
And all the rest
He taught with passion
And created interest

We'd have a special word
One every day
Big juicy ones
Not easy to say

Pugnacious, vivacious
Gregarious, pusillanimous
But the one I'd use to describe him
Would simply be magnanimous

He was calm and caring
And gave positive vibes
These we will take
Through our lives

For an adult he was
Really quite cool
He taught me the pen
Is the ultimate tool

Thank you Mr M
You truly are cool
And by far the best teacher
Throughout the whole school.

Shakeel Rahman (11)

Which One Is My Favourite Person?

I have my favourite people
All in a row.
But which one's my favourite?
How will I know?

Eeyore is my friend,
Eeyore is my neighbour,
He's on a children's programme
Where I watch him labour.

My furry friend is Poco-polie,
His real name is my friend Rolie.
He's a little dog with big floppy ears
And when my brother screams,
I wonder how he hears.

I have a little brother,
His nickname is 'Bug'.
He calls me 'Rachael Bug',
Then gives me a great big hug!

My mum, my mum,
How could this be?
I love my mum better than me.
She looks after me when things go wrong,
And takes me to hospital when I'm not strong.
She even does the washing and that will pong.

The best is my mum!
I choose her because she is fun.
She doesn't boss me around to do this and that,
She makes me wear a hat in fact!

Rachael Brown (9)

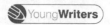

My Grandad's Moments, My Favourite Person

My grandad hopped on a bike
With his trousers in his socks,
When he looks after me,
He keeps an eye on the clock.

He sits in the kitchen
Doing a crossword every day,
Wondering whether
This time it might pay.

He fishes for algae
In his non-fish pond,
Eats chocolate digestives
Of which he is fond.

He listens to cricket
On the wind-up radio,
Whilst my grandma nags him
To turn the volume down low . . .

We had a celebration
For my mum's degree,
And he dropped champagne
On my grandma's knee!

This is my grandad
That's funny and kind,
And he has the most
Amazing mind.

Georgia Hardy (11)

My Favourite Person - Haiku

B en is so funny!
E nd of the day he's such fun
N ever to be sad.

Lauren Gallacher (10)

20

A Friend A Million Miles Away

Who is my special person?
Mum, Dad, brother, sister . . . dog?
No! No! No! It's my best friend!
Every time I see her, I smile,
Every second I am with her is worthwhile.
She fills my day with happiness and joy.
She's not only a friend . . .
She's my cousin too!
That's what gives her a special touch.
I love her very much.

I've had lots of friends in the past,
But they never seemed to last.
I only see her once a year,
That's what makes her ever so dear.
Caring, friendly, cheery and fun!
Kind, trustworthy, helpful and loving,
She's everything you could want from a cousin.
A strong bond is something we share.

She is always there for me!
With a cheery smile and a loving heart.
Every time I remember her,
Happy memories flood my mind,
She is so sweet and kind.
It's hard to keep a friend so close . . .
When they're a million miles away!
But there's one thing I know for sure,
Forever and ever best friends we will stay!

Savini Hewage (11)

My Family

I love my sister
So very much
So very much
I love my sister
So very much
Indeed

I love my mum
I love my mum
Because
She is beautiful
She is beautiful
She's the greatest
Mum on Earth

I love my dad
I love my dad
He's the greatest
Dad on Earth
He's cool
And he loves me
So much

I love my brother
I love my brother
He's good at football
He can do five kick ups
And can dribble the ball

And now I'm done!

Stephanie Poon (10)

My Daddy

He cares for me and my sister too,
He works so hard, all week through,
He puts us first, in every way,
He's the very best, that's what I say,
My daddy, my friend.

We play lots of games, on many days,
We lie in the sunshine, soaking up rays,
We love chess because it's fun,
We go outside, to the park and run,
My daddy, my friend.

He is a doctor, a surgeon you know,
He does operations and has to sew,
He has a cool job, an important one,
He's a clever man, I'm glad I'm his son,
My daddy, my friend.

We laugh together, he says funny things,
We have a great time, especially when he sings!
We have fun in our house, whenever he's around,
We laugh and laugh, it's a lovely sound,
My daddy, my friend.

He's the best man I know, that much is true,
He beats the rest, the whole world through,
He's great, he's fun, he's all I need,
He's my favourite person, oh yes indeed,
My daddy, my friend.

Oscar Saharoy (8)

True Red

I was born a true red,
They are always in my heart and head,
My destiny, my passion and my pride,
Liverpool Football Club are the world's greatest side.

Sami Patel (9)

23

The Mummy Appreciation Poem!

My mummy is great because,
even though sometimes she shouts,
she cooks us good meals and
when we pout, she sends us to bed
with a story in our head.

My mummy is fab because,
even though she tells us off,
she makes great cakes and
when we scream
she handles the scene.

My mummy is awesome because,
even though she cries,
she is the most amazing,
fandabidozzie mummy
in all the world!

And I love her to bits because
she cooks and bakes,
to make us cakes,
she sends us to bed
with a story in our head.

And when we scream
she handles the scene.
I love my mummy
for all different things, but mainly
because she loves me.

Briony Tripp (11)

My Favourite Person

My favourite friend is Poco-Poliie
His real name is my friend Rollie
I really love it when he laughs
When he watches me doing crafts.

Emily Brown (6)

My Pudding Sister

My sister is a pudding,
She loves and loves to eat
And when the day is done,
She snuggles under her sheet.

I love my baby sister
And I'm sure she loves me too,
But the one thing I hate doing,
Is changing her nappy of poo!

You may think she's cute,
All cuddly and sweet,
But when she starts crying,
She's a real treat!

I love her little smile,
I love her little giggle,
But the thing I love the most,
Is the way she does the wiggle.

Now there is a sad part
At the end of my lovely song,
When I can't stop her crying,
When I don't know what's wrong.

My sister is a pudding,
All cuddly and sweet,
I love her down to her toes,
Yes I love her down to her feet.

Hollie Belford (11)

My Mum

My favourite person is caring, beautiful and loving,
She is the one that cures my nightmares
And gives me dreams of love and joy
And thinks of everyone else before herself,
She loves me very much, she is my mum.

Bethany McNerlin (10)

My Mum Is My Hero

My mum is my hero,
she's so precious to me,
so forget old Superman,
and listen to me.

Go talk to your mum,
there's no need to be scared,
and thank her for all the love she has shared.

Or why don't you think?
Thinking is good,
because all of these things you should have understood:

She gives you praise when you're good,
when it starts to rain she pulls up your hood.
When you're making your way to bed one night,
she's the one who's there to stop the frights.
She looks after you when you are sick,
she builds you a home, brick by brick.
She takes you to school so you can learn,
why can't you do something in return?

Listen, all I'm trying to say,
is think of all those bills she must pay.
Caring for family is hard enough,
so I think her job is pretty tough.

My mum is my favourite my a mile,
because she's the one who makes me smile!

Jemma Wolfe (11)

My Papa

My papa has gone away
He has gone to Heaven to stay
I miss my papa every day
I hope and pray that some day
I will meet my papa again.

Megan Burns (11)

My Cat

She's cute and cuddly,
round and fat,
fuzzy and soft,
she's my cat!

She's loyal and friendly,
kind and pretty,
warm and cosy,
she's my kitty!

She's got beautiful eyes,
and a sweet little face,
one white mitten,
she's my kitten!

She's brave and bold,
she ain't no wuss,
big and strong,
she's my puss!

Her name is Amber,
who I won't forget,
she definitely is . . .
my favourite pet!

She's good and gorgeous,
a fantastic feline,
a beautiful kitty,
and she's *mine!*

Kate Blundel (11)

My Fave Person

My fave person is in my family
She's as bright as the sun
And makes . . .
Me have so much fun
My fave person is my mum!

Georgia Talman (9)

My Favourite Person

I wonder who is my favourite person?
A very hard choice to make.
From friends and family to celebrities,
Which category should I take?

The sort of people I really like
Are ones who are thoughtful and kind.
But searching high and low everywhere,
They are so hard to find!

I like them if they're always cheerful,
Positive and funny,
Who don't really care too much
About fame and money.

I think I've got a good idea
Who my person is,
It's someone who lives far away,
Someone who I miss.

I like that type of character,
So friendly and warm,
Like there's a bright sun over them,
As yellow as sweetcorn.

I know who my favourite person is,
No one could be finer,
It is my lovely grandmother,
Who lives away in China!

Rachel Fu (13)

My Mum Helps Me Through

My mum is there when I am sad,
When I need her help, when I yelp.
My mum is always there
When I need her most.
My mum is my favourite person in the world!

Leah Duery (13)

My Favourite Person Ever

Who is my favourite person?
Let me think . . .
Maybe the great tap dancer
From the kitchen sink!

Maybe my best friend;
Anyone will do!
Or it could be my science teacher?
My gorgeous cats too!

It could be my sister,
Rebecca,
Nah, my uncle
Would be better!

How about my friend
From up the road?
Or maybe even Sammy!
(He's my pet toad)

A celebrity?
But who could it be?
How about my second cousin,
Stephanie?

In fact I'll just settle
For who I like the most.
The mailman:
He delivers my morning post!

Bethany Carter (10)

Gipsey The Slobbery Dog

Oh Gipsey no dog is as slobbery as you,
You slobber so much I don't know what to do.
I think that my fingers are going to turn into goo,
I love you so much, even when you smell of poo!

Aaron Dean (10)

Glorious Dad!

My favourite person,
But who to pick?
Friend or family,
Now this is a trick.

I have a friend called Oliver,
Now he is my best friend.
He'll make a joke of all of you,
But only for pretend.

There is just one more person,
He is also very friendly.
That person is my dad,
So not that trendy.

So who shall I make my poem about?
I'll make it about my dad!
He's funny but sometimes overdoes it,
But only by a tad.

He likes working on his computer,
Making animations.
Sometimes he would make a plane,
Flying across the nations.
So now that I've told you about my dad,
It's time to say the word.
The word that means the opposite to hi,
It's time to say *goodbye!*

Sheldon Delices (11)

My Little Westie

Sadie is my dog and she is very kind
But there is one thing, she's got a stubborn mind
She sleeps all day and she sleeps all night
She won't go for a walk without a fight.

Victoria Towersey (9)

My Mystical Mysti
(My favourite person 2009 is Mysti my guinea pig)

With fairy-lIke features
You're the queen of all creatures
There is no sign of lies
They'll never shine in your eyes
You act all posh 'n' wise
And it's always a surprise to see your nose so pink
And I do so wonder what you think.

You just sit there like an angel
Upon my lap so warm
You never say anything unkind to me
(Not that you say anything at all!)
No one could replace you
Your personality is fine
In fact, I find it perfect
It's a duplicate of mine!

So I'd just like to say
In my own special way
How much you mean to me
You fill my life with glee
So here's a reason why
You pick me up and put me high

You're just so wonderful in all that you do
And that is why I love you.

Isabel Black (10)

My Brother Sam

Sam is my brother
And my best friend
Most of the day we like to play
Maybe we fight in the middle of the night
Yet we always make up
And best friends we will always stay.

Daniel Phillips (9)

My Favourite Person 2009

Abbie is one of my best friends
She loves to play board games and have fun
We play in my tree house for hours on end
She loves playing a variety of musical instruments

Leah is one of my best friends
She loves to run about and talk
Her hair is red, curly and luscious
She loves swimming just like a mermaid

Ellis is one of my best friends
She loves to have themed sleepovers
And annoy her twin Ben
She loves making things and is very creative

Alix is one of my best friends
She loves the colour baby blue
A football star and a great dancer
She loves to make yummy things to eat

Megan is one of my best friends
She loves her dog Kiza and chocolate Minstrels
Camping out with her is fun
She loves her dolphin bedroom

Out of all of my friends, I could not pick one
They are all so different but also so much fun
I hope you agree.

Sophie Mill (11)

My Mother Is The Best

M y mother is the best in the whole world.
O n my birthday she gives me lots and lots of presents.
T oday and tomorrow she will be my favourite person.
H aving a mother like mine makes me special.
E veryone would love to have a mother like mine.
R emember mothers are one of the best people in the world.

Madia Rehman (10)

Philip Pullman - My Favourite Person

When the inventor of the Alethiometer
Decided to bring us on its journey
Not one of us could have possibly imagined
What he had.
None of us could have known how this path could be
So twisting, so shocking, so dangerous.

From the start we are joined by Lyra and Pantalaimon,
Whose true father is he,
King of lorek Byrnison and Lord of Asriel,
Forger of the subtle knife.

Along the way we will meet, and lose, new friends,
Such as Will, Lee Scorsby and Mary Malone.
It will be the same with their enemies,
Like Mrs Coulter, the sinister spectres of Cittàgazze
And the angel Metatron.

Those who join him on his journey will be
Thrown through windows in cosmic matter to new universes
And travel down ancient highways of frozen lava
On the backs of alien creatures.
They will even be led to the realm of death itself . . .

This isn't even a handful of where
My favourite person, Philip Pullman, can take you.
His stories will blow us away, so only the Dust is left.

Philippa Rose Humphreys (10)

My Sister, Sophie

S ometimes silly
O utstanding and
P retty
H onest and
I ncredible
E verything a sister should be.

Samantha Widdas (9)

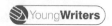

Untitled

I looked so anxiously into the cage
Thought I'd have a hamster for a change.
'Hey, let's get this one,' my brother said, 'he looks so sad.'
It was a shame, he looked like my dad.
Then from nowhere the little guy came
Right up to the window in search of fame
His golden fur shone as bright as the sun
And his cheeky grin looked so much fun.
I dropped on my knees for a closer peep
Whilst my brother suggested one with fur like a sheep.
He picked up his nuts and began to gorge
I was having this one and I would call him George.

My hamster George is the cutest creature,
His silky fur being his greatest feature,
He sits in his house only showing his nose
Which by far is his most favourite pose.
I don't like this view obstructed by a bar
So now I roll him round in a little toy car,
I whizz him around all over the floor,
Oh life with George is never a bore.
This is why I love him all so dearly,
I could not stress this any more sincerely,
Which is why I am certain that
George is by far my most favourite person!

Sophie Kidder (10)

Chloe

Chloe is as soft as can be . . .
Her fur is the colour of milk chocolate,
She speaks to you when you stroke her,
In a funny sort of purr,
Her hot, fishy breath wafts up your nose as she walks past,
Her tail is a furry rope, as strong as ever,
Chloe, my nan's cat, is the best cat I've ever seen.

Ellissa Millard (11)

My Cousin's Dog

My best friend is my cousin's dog
He bounces round just like a frog
Frodo is this clown's name
He likes to play a lot of games
He pricks his ears and jumps about
If he thinks we're all going out
Throw his ball and off he goes
To bring it back to our toes
He loves to jump, leap and play
Barking and splashing all the day
In the park, while it is dark
Frodo's habit is chasing rabbits
The trampoline he finds great fun
If short of time instead of a run
His soft, white fur is full of spots
We try to count how many he's got
Watch out for his long, thin tail
Hit by it, you'll really wail
Frodo has a friend called Ted
He's supposed to sleep with but instead
When all is quiet and we've gone to bed
He creeps up by me and lays his head
On the pillow next to mine
We really have a lovely time.

Chelsea Stemp (10)

My Best Bud

My mum's motto,
Means a lotto.
She says, 'Learn something new each day!'
Which I think will take me a long way . . .
Through the path of life . . .
And strife,
That may come my way.

She says she has a double chin
But it adds to her infectious grin.
I love her hugs . . .
And the good stuff she brings in mugs,
When I am ill
To soothe a wintry chill.

If I had a genie,
I would need just one wish.
That my mum be made an angel or fairy,
So she does all her great deeds,
And fulfils all needs.
Her wand steady and ready
With just a swish, swish!

Charlotte Fisher (9)

Daisy

Daisy, she's my favourite pet, my best friend.
I cuddle her and play with her.
She sleeps in her bed, all nice and comfy.
She has a nice juicy bone once in a while,
I pet her and lift her up.

Daisy, she's my dog, my only dog,
My favourite dog.

Lucas Claxton (8)

My Favourite Person/Dog

When we got her she was minute,
So energetic and so cute.
Such a cuddly friend to see,
But as hyper as a bumblebee.
She got used to her new home
And never ever even moved.
She doesn't take well to toys
And destroys them, making a load of noise.
Her tail wags when she hears us coming,
And all of a sudden she starts her running.
She runs really fast,
Making every leap last and last.
When the sun glistens on her brown fur,
Making her even more beautiful than when we got her.
She likes us all in our own unique way,
And never gets bored, not even for one single day.
When we go out for just a little while, there she will lay,
Hoping we are on our way.
When we step through the door,
She jumps up quickly, showing her paw.
She licks us from head to toe,
Hoping we will never go.
That day when we went to pick her we knew straight away,
That the dog we had picked was with us to stay.

Hannah Tiffany (10)

Shannon

S he is my best friend for life
H ad a great summer with her
A t sleepovers she is funny
N ever mind about your worries, she will cheer you up
N othing will break us up
O r make us sad, my best friend and I
N ow that is what I love about her.

Kelsey Scott (10)

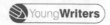
My Brother

My brother is not fat,
He is not as small as a rat.

He's not as tall as an elephant,
But that is not relevant.

He's not as skinny as a twig,
But he is certainly not that big.

Sometimes he's not happy,
But is normally very clappy.

He is never ever bad,
But sometimes he can be sad.

My brother is not very strong,
But he is never wrong.

He is not really weak,
And he is not a freak.

He sometimes can be lazy,
But is definitely not crazy.

Even though he is young,
He is certainly not dumb.

Sometimes he is a sight,
But for me he is just right.

Lewis Green (11)

My Favourite Person

My sister Grace
Has very good taste
She's very smart
And good at art
She's amazing Grace
And has a beautiful face
My sister Grace.

Laura Dawe (9)

My Fabulous Father

My fabulous father gets me clothes
And buys me sweets

Gives me pocket money
And always cuddles me

My daddy takes me out
And we always eat out on a Friday night

I make my daddy coffee
Because he loves the way I make it

My daddy tucks me into bed
And always reads interesting books to me

I love my daddy
He is really, really funny

He tell me stories and jokes
That make me laugh a lot

I enjoy the company of my daddy
Because he makes me feel like a star

My daddy is the best
Because he beats the rest

I am his only daughter
Who brings him all the laughter!

Zainab Faruqi (10)

Mrs Shaw

Oh Mrs Shaw, you're so nice like snow and ice
You do art because you're smart
You're quite old but your clothes are bright and bold
You dress neat and have pretty shoes on your feet
You like school and you're so cool
You're strong and never wrong
When I moved class you said goodbye and I cried.

Chelsea Gault (9)

My Dad

My family is great!
Sometimes they let me stay up late!
My dad is the best,
Like him better than the rest because . . .
He lets me sit on his shoulders
Without a word of complaint,
He plays noughts and crosses with me
But he always wins the game,
He lets me go on the computer
For a very long time,
He takes me out to town to Toys R Us
Sometimes he doesn't take my brother
Because he is more mature than me!
I don't want to be like him,
I think he is mean and immature!
Mum is great too but . . .
She can never carry me on her shoulders,
She can never whirl me about,
She doesn't let me go on the computer
For very long,
She takes me out to town but *never* to Toys R Us.

I like my dad best though,
Shh, don't tell the rest!

Ellie Kelly (11)

An Ode To The Liverpool Captain

Steven Gerrard is so class
he is the master of the pass.

He plays for Liverpool
his right foot's not a bad tool.

Not often does he fail
his pace means the defence
can only follow his tail.

His vision is amazing
his skill is hair-raising.

I'll tell you he's worth more
than twenty million pounds
with ease the defence he weaves around.

Our Stevie he ain't no fool
he can bend a free kick round any wall.

Stevie's powerful shots, they hit the net
all supporters love him when met.

For regularly he scores
and makes the Kop stand roar.

Gerrard is a football king
he wants to hear you all sing.

Callum Loader (10)

My Best Friend

My best friend is called Kiera and she is the very best,
Kiera is pretty and likes to go to the city,
She is cool and likes school and isn't a fool,
She defends me but never offends me,
She is always funny and likes to spend money
and wants it to be sunny,
Also she is fun but doesn't like to run but she acts and dances,
But Kiera is a super duper best friend.

Sophie Sarney (10)

Friend

What makes a friend?
An ear to hear?
An eye to see?
A leg to walk on?
An arm to pick up with?
No . . . !
What makes a friend?
Pretty, good looking?
Glamorous, glittery?
Perfect and popular?
Skinny and fashionable?
No . . . !
What makes a friend?
Listens to the latest track?
The latest celeb haircut?
The best at everything?
The latest toys in her wardrobe?
No . . .!
A friend loves you for being you!
A friend comforts you in your sadness!
A friend should be there for you,
Even at the toughest times!
Just like Ellie!

Bryony Amelia Mead (11)

My Favourite Person

She loves to play football,
She loves playing with friends,
She really loves her family
And also loves her friends!

Me and her are BFFs and always will be,
We always have sleepovers,
We have a few snacks and then watch DVDs
And then we stay up till late.

Stephanie Hall (10)

The Best Mum Ever!

My mum is the best mum ever,
For she is always there for me,
She is very, very beautiful
And I always love what she is wearing.

Whenever I am sick,
I can't get out of bed,
My mum is always there to say,
You don't worry I will take care of you.

She is always fun and active
And loves to play with me,
She is the best mum ever,
For she is always there for me.

My mum is always cooking,
My mum is always cleaning,
I try to keep the house the right way round,
But it always turns back upside down.

My mum loves to play with me,
And she is very fun,
We like to play Scrabble,
We like to play Monopoly
And that is why she is the best mum ever!

Rhea Sokhi (9)

Great Uncle

He has a warm heart
He is kind, caring
Sweet as chocolate
He is loving
He has time for me

He is as fast as the wind
He has a big smile
Everything about him is cool.

Amanda Masuku (11)

You Expect Me To Choose!

My favourite person
You expect me to choose.

My favourite person
Or people should I say?
Are the people I love
And are there every day.

The people who will be there
Through thick and thin
My family and friends
Who did you think?

Those are the people
I cherish and love
Who will be there
No matter what.

They love me for who I am
And not what I've got.

So there you have it
That's how it goes
My family and friends
Are the people I chose!

Eden O'Shea-Price (10)

Tremendous Tigger

My furry friend is very sweet
She loves a head-scratch and a treat
She hops all day, she hops all night
Sometimes our dogs give her a fright
She loves to lie down in the sun
When she plays she's very fun
She loves carrots, she loves grass
When she hops, she's very fast
She loves to play with her toy
When people come she's very coy
Her fur is a hazy brown
When I clean her, she gives a frown
She loves to munch on chocolate drops
If she eats any more she's going to pop
The cutest part of her is her eyes
I think she needs a bit more exercise
She likes to chew on a wire
By sundown she's starting to tire
She's very gentle and very nice
In the winter, she's as cold as ice
She loves to nibble on a snack
I love her, she loves me back!

Tazmin Clements (10)

Grandma Is Great

Grandma makes me happy whenever I am sad.
Every time she talks to me I listen to her carefully.
Most things my grandma says are really, really old,
Like the least said the best mended,
Which I never really understand,
But now I realise it means,
If you keep it shut no one will get into trouble.
My grandma's great and I love her.

Faye Pollard (11)

Stan

My dog is called Stan,
I'm his biggest fan.
When we go for a walk,
I wish he could talk!

When I'm sad, he makes me happy,
Even when he's mad and yappy!
We go to the park,
He sees the ducks and loves to bark!

When my mum's on the phone,
He's very noisy eating his bone.
This makes Mum cross and she has a moan
And shouts at him in a serious tone!

He sneaks upstairs and hides in my bed,
When I wake up, he's laying on my head.
He doesn't like cats, or people in hats,
But he is very good at catching rats.

He is only small but loves to play football,
He also jumps really high over the wall.
Stan is my best mate,
I think he's really great!

Joshua Slate (11)

The Greatest Of All

When I received this letter,
Simply asking for me,
To write about my favourite person,
I thought, *who could my inspiration be?*

I'm a very sensitive girl you see,
I didn't want to offend,
My mum, my dad, my grandma,
My granddad, my brother, my best friend.

But then I sat and *really* thought,
I can't decide on just one!
Because my family are all special in different ways,
They're all kind, and loving and fun!

My mum is kind-hearted and loving,
My dad is unique and fun,
My grandparents are reassuring and caring,
And as far as brothers go, mine's number one!

My family are the ones who are inspiring,
The ones to pick me up when I fall,
My family are always there for me,
They are the greatest of all!

Georgia Thorpe (11)

Doctor Who

D avid Tennant is my favourite person
O h how good an actor he is
C ybermen are his enemies
T he TARDIS is his time machine
O h everyone loves him
R egeneration

W ho are you?
H ello Matt Smith
O h how I love Doctor Who.

Aimee Wells (7)

Shottle Norah

I have a favourite person,
She's different from the rest.
She is simply my best friend
And really just the best.

Her name is Shottle Norah,
She chews her cud all day
And says hello to my sister, Laura,
When they go out to play.

We take her to the shows,
Red ribbons she has won,
Beating all the others
'Cause she is number one.

Maybe it's now time
To tell you what she is,
To save your mind from exploding,
'Cause of this puzzling quiz.

Her name is Shottle Norah,
She is my favourite cow.
She is in the parlour
Producing milk right now!

Emily Barrett (11)

My Dog Paddy Wags

P retty
A mazing
D ozing
D og
Y ou're

W hat
A ll
G irls
S hould have.

Chloe Dooley (10)

Determination

Have you ever heard of Emily Pankhurst?
Well, unfortunately her story ends in the worst,
but first let me tell you how she became
a very well-known historic name . . .

Emily was born in 1852
and since then had always wanted to do
something to change every woman's life,
no longer would they be just a simple wife.

Every single day she would protest,
to try and beat the men and pests,
always determined, she never gave slack,
she kept on going, and never looked back.

Then one day, in a hurry,
Emily went to a race course in Surrey,
while the king's horse came speeding by,
Emily ran in front with a sign.

On that awful day, she died,
but Emily Pankhurst died with pride.
She gave up her own future,
so every other woman could have a happy one.

Rosalind Henderson (11)

He's Just Great!

There was a man who I knew,
He was extremely gifted and talented too,
He used to give me sweets and more,
He spread love and care for all.

He was a superb mentor,
A stupendous achiever,
He was clearly the best,
He was my grandad,
Who is always better than the rest.

Ishrath Iqbal (11)

Gop

My favourite person is my grandad,
He doesn't get cross when I am bad.
The word 'Gop' became his name,
No one else is called the same.

I know he lives quite far away,
But I love it when I go and stay.
I go on holiday for about a week,
I can pick up the phone whenever I need to speak.

He likes vehicles, especially trains,
And he has a lot of brains!
He takes me out in his car,
Wherever I want, even if it's far.

He sometimes can't hear what I say,
But I tend to say it anyway!
He doesn't really have much hair,
Which means his head is nearly bare!

We will always be together,
For ever and ever and ever!
As you can probably see,
I love him and he loves me!

Hannah Ransom (10)

Mum And Dad

There are two people who love me, when I'm mad.
They are called my mum and dad.

There are two people who smile, even without the sun.
They are called my dad and mum.

There are two people who love me, even when I am a bit bad.
They are called my mum and dad.

There are two people who are always fun.
They are called my dad and mum.

Isabella Atherley (10)

The Rubster And Me

The Rubster and me play in the morning,
We play after lunch,
Or at afternoon play.
We play any time of the day.

We practise netball,
Play our recorders,
Help out in the classroom
Or sing in the school choir.

We might be top secret spies
Or roll around in the field,
We might be dogs or horses,
Rats, cats, anything we feel like.

We'd play if it was cloudy,
Or even if it was windy.
We'd play if there was sun,
Or when there's lots of rain.

Whatever we play,
Whatever the time of day,
Whatever the weather,
It's always just the Rubster and me!

Sophie Le Feuvre (9)

My Little Sister

Although I never realise this,
She is always by my side,
Even if we fight a lot,
She makes me happy when I cry.
She's clever and imaginative
And I never get bored,
For with my little sister,
She's the big one
And I'm the small!

Ophelia Morley (10)

Untitled

My favourite person is my little sister,
She has the loveliest hair,
And whenever I lose something,
She always has one to spare.

It's so much fun to have a sister,
Although it depends which kind.
My sister is the number one,
The one that's hard to find.

She loves going shopping
'Cause she gets to buy a lot of things,
And it's so funny when it's her bedtime,
'Cause instead of going to bed, she sings.

She has a wonderful choice
When it comes to clothes,
In fact sometimes I let her pick mine,
She's never let me down.

She loves it when I give her a backie on my bike,
As we *swish* past the wind just like a kite.
I say, 'Don't worry, Amelia!' and she just holds on tight,
And that tells me I'm definitely doing something right!

Jovarn Blair (11)

My Favourite Person

My favourite person is Theo my nephew
he walks, he talks
he giggles, he wiggles
he's small not tall
he likes toys and noise
he cries and sighs
he toddles and waddles
he poos and moos
he's grumpy and plumpy.

Jami Harris (9)

Friendship

Smile, smile, smile,
I've had a friend for a while.
I think she's kind but can be cheeky,
I always see her weekly.

Jump, jump, jump,
When she hits her head with a thump.
While running away from mice,
Which isn't very nice.

School, school, school,
We both think it's very cool,
We have lots of fun at playtime,
Where we love to make up a rhyme.

Friends, friends, friends,
We have the same kind of trends,
We both like drawing,
When we're older we want to go touring.

Tara, Tara, Tara,
She always waves shouting, 'Torah!'
She can be so very crazy,
Sometimes she can be a bit lazy.

Amy Gunning (11)

My Little Sis!

My favourite person is my little sis, she's 2, tanned with corkscrew hair
Although she's cute you can sometimes go amiss
Cos when she wants to she can get into mischief
Leave her alone with anything, anything at all
Like a permanent marker and there'll be scribbles on the wall
Or a glass of water, it'll soon be on the floor
As I'm the big sister she'll be knocking on my door
But nothing beats that little smile or the sloppy kiss at night
Or when she runs to give me a full on hug, when she sees my face in sight.

Chloe Lloyd (11)

Charlie

My favourite person is Charlie,
This little bird is quite barmy,
He is three months old,
He is brave and bold,
That is my budgie called Charlie.

This mischievous bird is fun,
If he could he'd fly up to the sun,
He'd fly right round,
Then land on a cloud,
And not stop until he was done.

He's blue and white,
Flies like a kite,
His majestic pattern,
Speaks like Latin,
To me it's another language.

His cage is his home,
His perch is his throne,
He's like many kings,
But he has wings,
Together he and his brother will roam.

Maisie Butcher (11)

My Favourite Person

My name is Lily and I am six,
I love my mum to absolute bits.
She makes me breakfast, dinner and tea,
And gives me big cuddles while I'm sitting on her knee.
She buys me teddies, toys and treats,
My favourite are my lemurs, which help me to sleep.
We go to the cinema and go to the park,
We snuggle up and watch DVDs when it gets dark.
She makes me laugh when I am sad,
She is my mummy and I'm really glad.

Lily Slater (6)

Ross

He is my cousin,
24 years of age,
He is good at writing
And good on stage.
His name is Ross.

He makes me laugh,
He is so funny!
He makes rainy days
Seem sunny.
His name is Ross.

He seems like a big kid,
All childish and fun,
He makes me smile
When the day is done.
His name is Ross.

He cheers me up
When I'm in knots,
He treats me well
And I love him lots.
His name is Ross.

Nicola Rose (11)

My Dad!

My favourite person is my dad,
But when I start dancing I make him mad.
Day after day he works like mad,
Digging, potting and snipping away,
So when he comes home he says to me,
'You better be grateful that I haven't broken my knee!'
Sometimes I think what a great dad he is,
He is kind, loving and sweet.
When my mum looks at him he makes her tweet!
Now I realise that I'm pretty neat.

Lydia Talman (10)

That's Why!

Great and happy
All the time
Playing together
We get along fine
That's my favourite person.

                    She loves to act
                    She loves to dance
                    She loves sport
                    It's a fact!
                    That's my favourite person.

Brave and smart
Funny too
Kind and caring
What about you?
That's my favourite person.

                    When I'm sad
                    She cheers me up
                    She'll make me laugh
                    And say, 'What's up?'
                    That's why she's my favourite person.

Rhian Bland (10)

I Have A Guinea Pig

I have a guinea pig that makes me smile you see.
Who is in my garden every day at tea.
His name is Bino and he is black and white.
He lives in his cage every day at night.
He is furry and cute and eats loads of carrots,
All healthy stuff you can ever imagine.
His favourite food is grass and broccoli.
He is small and long and his teeth are tiny.
He is as gentle as a flower and Bino is my pet
And my pet alone.

Shalayka Shephard (10)

Tigger

Tigger, the cat, is really fat
Never happy, always hiding under the mat
But I still love my cat

I always loved it when he used to purr
When I stroked his fur

Cats are the best
They outnumber the rest
But my cat is special

He always used to make me laugh
When he used to jump in my bath

Now he is old and lazy
His eyesight is hazy

His bones are sore
He won't run fast anymore

I miss the way he used to run when he saw a dog
Now he can't even see through fog

I still love him
Even though he has broken his limb.

Alida Evans (13)

My Best Friend

B est friends are cool
E very kid wants one
S ometimes they're imaginary
T ime to tell you about my best friend

F irst she is nice
R ight until the end
I ntelligent and smart
E very single day
N ow her name is Rachael
D ay and night we'll always be best friends.

Danielle Greengrass (11)

My Best Friend Sniffles

My best friend is my hamster
he is warm and nice to cuddle
when he is in a great big huddle.

My hamster makes me laugh a lot
he always makes me lose the plot
when I'm sad and feeling bad
I get him out and he walks about.

My hamster is ginger and white
he goes on his wheel all through the night
he makes lots of noise all night long
and really annoys everyone!

My hamster is fun, my hamster is cute
my hamster is small and loves it in the ball
my hamster means a lot to me
he is my pet only.

We have fun all the time
mostly in the night-time
I love him so much
he is my best friend - *Sniffles!*

Eve Bishop (10)

Who Is My Favourite Person?

My favourite person is a celebrity

She is cute like a kitten
I love the songs she has written

She is small and petite
She is very sweet

I love the clothes she wears
I also like her hair

My favourite person is Lady Gaga
When I grow up I want to be like her.

Bethany Bristol (9)

My Love

My love's eyes are like
Lovely shining stars in the night sky.

My love's lips are like
Sweet red cherries that I want to try.

My love's skin is as
Smooth as a white dove's feather.

My love's hair is like golden silk,
Much better quality than leather.

My love, my love, my love.

Alexander Bojic-Aguilar (10)

Toddlers

Now I know you think that I
Will talk about my mum,
There'll probably be some toddler,
Who'll talk about his bum!

But oh no, I say,
Oh no, come see,
A girl who once said,
'Look, a bumblebee!'

She's not too big and not too small,
(Well, actually, she's two feet tall!)
The bouncy ball, the doll, the bear,
'Oh look! Barbie's wearing no underwear!'

She doesn't like guns though doesn't mind
A quick brawl!
That little toddler
The driver-up-the-wall!

So now I put in front of thee,
My family, my cat, and my sister,
Beshlie.

Jacob Seelochan (11)

My Favourite Person, My Best Friend

My favourite person
In the whole wide world
Is my best friend
And no, it's not a girl.

His name is Liam,
He is nine years old,
He makes me laugh,
He makes me smile,
I've known him for quite a while.

We've known each other
Since we were three,
When Liam moved in
Next door to me.

He lives with his nana
And dog, called Squiggle.
What a cool name,
It makes me giggle.

We became the best of friends.
Our friendship will never end.

Elisha Wraith (9)

My Cousin Florence

F olding me in a hug when I arrive.
L oves to play with my toys, aged 101.
O ften very merry and always kind.
R elating the stories of your childhood.
E yesight not very good.
N ecklace to call for help.
C akes on a tray for us to enjoy.
E at them all!

I remember and miss you Florence,
The favourite of all my relatives.

Thomas Stephens (8)

My Mum

My mum is great,
My mum's never late,
My mum's my best mate.

My mum's fast,
My mum's never last,
My mum's always up for a task.

My mum's the best,
My mum's a great chef,
My mum's never left.

My mum's always there,
My mum will always care,
My mum always shares.

My mum is great,
My mum's never late,
My mum's my best mate.

My mum's my mum
And I'm happy she's my mum
Because I love her loads.

Angel Osei-Kissi (10)

My Favourite Person

My favourite person is Gemma
She has brown, curly hair
And blue, pearly eyes
We go to school together
We play Camogie every Saturday
Me and Gemma will be best friends forever.

Rhianna McCaffrey (9)

My Favourite Neopets

My favourite girl Neopet is Sophie the swamp witch.
She has two brothers and lives in a deep ditch.
My favourite boy Neopet is the Nightsteed.
He's always stealing the things he needs.
My favourite person is me.
I'm very good cos I'm Keri!

Keri Heddle (8)

Ode To Misha

I envy your attractive appearance and your marvellous mind,
Misha, my dear, you are truly one of a kind.
When I am trapped and all alone,
I don't just feel bad and moan,
I think of your sweet company,
For that, and that alone is what comforts me.
Your eyes are like golden stars with perfect pupils,
But still, you gaze into my own dull eyes like they are jewels,
When I am crying, or I am blue
It's you who cheers me up Misha, it's you!
When I feel your velvety coat,
You purr like the engine of a speed boat,
If someone is troubling you, they better beware,
For, before you can blink, I will be there,
To protect you, and to love you forever,
For a time when I loathe you will come never.
Misha, you are my one true friend,
For if our friendship is broken, it's easy to mend,
When I first saw you, you flew like a dart,
And you stayed where you landed, deep inside my heart.

Penelope Young (11)

My Mum And Dad

My mum's the only one to care,
As she sits in her rocking chair.
She stares at the sea and sky
And never looks me in the eye.
I love her lots and lots and lots,
Because she makes me flowerpots.
I love her because she's my mum,
Even if she's got a big bum!

What can I say about Dad?
He's not the type to be sad.
He thinks he is funny,
He's got a big tummy.
What else can I say about him?

He drives his beautiful car.
His car will take him far.
He likes to eat meat.
He's got smelly feet.
He won't make you sad,
That's all I can say about Dad!

Maizie Ferrett (10)

Rafael Nadal

R eaches for his dream
A dorable
F it as Usain Bolt
A wesome at everything
E xample for everyone
L ively on court

N ever gloats
A n amazing tennis player
D rives Federer mad
A great athlete
L ovely to speak to.

Dana Kenneally-Forrester (10)

My Favourite Person!

My favourite person,
She kisses me on the head,
She turns off the light,
She tucks me into bed.

My favourite person,
Talks to me and sings,
She listens to me well,
She pretends I have wings.

My favourite person,
She's always sewing and cooking,
She loves to do hair,
She's always being nosey and looking.

My favourite person,
Is brilliant at pool,
She's always embarrassing
But can be awesome and cool.

My favourite person,
My mum!

Summer Valentine (11)

Gonzo

Gonzo is my owl,
He certainly is not foul.

Gonzo is light grey,
He is good at catching prey.

Gonzo is not very wise,
He has wide orange eyes.

Gonzo has large feet,
They can only just stand the heat.

Gonzo is the best,
But now he needs a rest.

Adam Dearsley (11)

My Parents

Yes it's my mum
    She isn't dumb
        She is kind
            So I've definitely got her mind!

She has good looks
    She also likes her books
        She's like a lizard lying in the sun
            She enjoys buying ice cream, oh yum-yum!
                Yes, it's my *mum!*

Now it's my dad
    He is quite mad!
        He is very strong
            Like King Kong!

He always has a smile on his face
    Even if it was the end of the human race!
        He works very hard
            Watching over me, my own private guard.
                Yes it's my *dad!*

Kishan Sharma (11)

My Mum

My mum, she is the very best,
She works so hard and never rests.
In the morning she shouts, 'Rise and shine,'
And asks me if I'm feeling fine.
She buys me treats when I am good
And prepares nice meals, because I love my food.
I love my mum with all my heart
And never, ever want to be apart.
Your mother's your mother
And mine is mine,
I will treasure all our memories
Of a mother's love so fine.

Lauren Quayle (6)

My Mum

My mum cooks very good meals
She looks divine and smells like roses in the garden
She is a very good nurse when I am ill
Her brain is as sharp as a shark's tooth
When my sister sees her eyes, they are as blue as the sky
On a summer's morning
My mum takes very good pride in her photos
Her photos are always top class
She has so many shoes you would lose count after twenty-five
She takes good pride in her fridge magnets
Which are all nice and beautiful like herself
Her hair is the best in the world
Because she is the best in the world
She is nearly always on the phone
She is always nice and kind
She is never horrible
She is never wrong because she is always correct
Because she is a know it all
She loves her films on TV.

Daniel Nunn (9)

My Sister Is My Best Friend

My sister is my best friend.
We argue and we fight
And all the time, she thinks she's right.
She might be a pain
And sometimes insane,
But I don't mind as long as she's by my side.
She has a great taste in style,
She's funny and groovy but
It's not about her style,
It's about her personality,
She's cool, lovely and kind.

I love you sis.

Cerys Paterson (9)

My Mum

She's got green eyes that glisten,
When I need to talk she'll listen,
Her voice is bold and strong,
Her hair is black and king of long,
Her smile is enlightening to see,
It's nice when it's just her and me!

My mum is one of a kind,
She's so pretty, she'll make you blind,
Me and my brother both agree,
That she's a sight we love to see,
And there's one thing I should tell you,
My mum's the best and there's nothing you can do!

Jordan Elizabeth Ellis (11)

My Daddy

My bed is full of sleep
My heart is content
To dream as I may
And wake when I will
Your hands fold like great wings about my face
And bring me full delight
When I think of friends I have met
Of the way that they went away
Like thin summer clouds melting in the air
You bend your head and wipe away a tear
When you go away
I am sad and lonely
But your love, kindness and sympathetic silence
Fills the house
At night by my bedside
Memories of your voice
Croon a sweet lullaby
So that I have new dreams
In my long, lonely rest.

Elaine Haripersaud (8)

My Best Friend

My best friend is as tall as a tree,
My best friend is as kind as you can be,
My best friend is as pretty as my mummy,
My best friend is as sharing as a bee,
My best friend is very kind to me,
My best friend's name is Rachel.

Isla Lury (9)

My Mum Is A Wonder

This person with me is my mother,
I love her,
She is a wonder.
So here's my story
Of my glory . . .
In the morning my mother works hard,
While she works I make her a card.
There is no other person who has the power
To make me brave the shower.
Who takes care of me when I'm ill?
My mother, of course, not a pill!
I help my mother water and grow
Flowers and bushes high and low.
When I grow up to be a man,
My dear mother will be a nan.
Who will look after her?
Why, me, her child,
Caring for her will be my pride.
My mother is a wonder . . .

Ishraq Choudhury Tasnim (9)

My Favourite Person

My favourite person is my best friend
'Cause she always makes me laugh.
She's always there when I am lost
And leads me on my path.
I've known her all my life,
That's why she's always there for me.
She's really kind to everyone,
If you knew her you would see.
I have lots of friends I like,
But I will keep not many,
But I know one thing,
I'll always be friends with Jenny.

Kelly Chowdhury (10)

My Favourite Person

My favourite person is my best friend,
although we are so different.

Like chalk and cheese,
like black and white.

Our hair is very different,
deep brown and golden blonde.

Our skin is also unlike,
natural tan and pale peach.

Passing little notes in class,
playing in the sun-warmed playground.

Millionaires with our own private jet
and fabulous clothes.

Or living in a haunted mansion,
with a man-eating werewolf.

I will never forget my favourite person,
because she is my best friend!

Leah Gibby (11)

My Best Friend Leanne

Leanne I really like
Because she gave me a great bike.
We do lots of things together,
I think we're going to be friends forever.
I like her so much,
We get in touch.
To dancing we both go,
Sometimes we put on a show.
At swimming we have fun,
After we have a bun.
I go to her house, she comes to mine,
Now we see each other all the time.

Lucy McGillivray (7)

Mum

My favourite person is my mum
She is so much fun.

She spoils me for giving me lots of sweets
and also giving me treats.

I always help my mum with cleaning
so she will have a happy feeling.

She is scared of heights
that gives her frights.

She nearly does all the chores
that makes her busier even more.

Her favourite colours are purple, blue and pink
but she doesn't know how to skate in the ice rink.

She is a lovely singer
and a great dancer.

My favourite person is my mum
she is so much *fun!*

Edriene Padua (8)

Bonkers!

My favourite person is Uncle Mark, he's just a great big child
You best watch out when he's around because he's really wild!
He'll pin us down on the floor and tickle us to death
Until we can take no more, then he'll let us take a breath
His Dizzee Rascal songs are rubbish
'Bonkers' all day long
And after the BBQ on Sunday, I'm so sick of that song
He lets the air out of bouncy castles
Until we squeal with joy
And gets told off by Uncle David as if he were a little boy
My uncle Mark, he cheers us up, even when we're sad
I couldn't live with him though, he'd just drive me mad.

Katie Dunning (11)

My Favourite Person

My favourite person is very bright,
They get every question absolutely right.

My favourite person is quite a delight,
They will never, ever put up a fight.

My favourite person always says, 'Night,' and then,
'Don't let the bed bugs bite.'

My favourite person is really quite light,
And they have got a little height.

My favourite person has good sight,
So they can see their artistic kite.

My favourite person really just might
Buy some jeans even if they're tight.

My favourite person has got to be my mum,
She is just very extremely bright!

I love my mum,
She is the best!

Megan Roberts (11)

That One Person

She is always there for me
when I'm feeling down.
Takes me to school and back again,
during work as well.
She helps me with my dancing
and my homework too.
We laugh and play together
all the day through.
Mummy does the best she can
every single day.
She is my favourite person
no matter what you say.

Amber Wollen (9)

My Lovely Funny Sister, Suzanna

When she plays in the garden,
She is lovely and always says, 'Pardon.'

She is always very polite,
And she's nice and bright.

She is to put the kettle on,
And I'm sad when she's gone.

She is very funny,
And she doesn't like her egg yolk too runny.

She's almost never sad
And very rarely bad.

She loves her caterpillar, Sally,
And can do a long shuttlecock rally.

She is only six,
And loves Weetabix.

Her favourite contestant in the X Factor is Eoghan,
And that is the end of the poem.

Francesca Cavadino (8)

My Favourite Person (ish!)

I guess you could say my favourite person
Isn't a person at all.
She really is quite furry
And likes to bat a ping-pong ball.
I love my little cat, Charlie,
I love her dearly, I do!
If you ever get the chance to meet her,
Then hey, lucky you!
She fights with her sister, Lola,
Literally all the time,
But I'm afraid my poem ends there,
'Cause I can't find any more words to rhyme!

Matthew Brooks (11)

My Grandad

My grandad loves his grub,
he also likes to go to the pub.

He likes to play his guitar,
and in his motor-home he travels far.

He has two dogs he likes to walk
and he loves to laugh, sing and talk.

He's very happy and makes me smile
and when he has his new hip he can walk for miles.

He often makes our family giggle
and when he walks his tummy wiggles.

My grandad loves to go on holiday
and when he takes me, I shout, *'Yay!'*

I miss him because he doesn't live near,
I love it when he comes to stay here.

My grandad is very clever and smart
and I love him with all my heart.

Lola Francis (10)

My Big Sister Grace

Grace and I both think alike, we're the two wheels on a bike.
And Grace will always be there, letting me know that she cares
We both know how to have fun, both of us love the sun.
And Grace will always be there, letting me know that she cares.
Whenever I feel like a cry, whenever there are tears in my eyes,
Grace will always be there, letting me know that she cares.
Whenever I'm in trouble, whenever I'm in need of a cuddle,
Grace will always be there, letting me know that she cares.
When Mum and Dad are mad, telling me that I'm bad,
Grace will always be there, letting me know she cares.
And even though she's far away and we don't see each other every day,
Grace will always be there, letting me know that she cares.

Anna Wernick (12)

My Favourite Person Is My Great Aunt!

My auntie Ann has very curly hair
If you be nice to her, she's very fair
She is just like a best friend
Even though she's much older than me
But she is still my friend
The best there ever will be.

My auntie Ann is the best
Much better than the rest
She is very funny
And I bet she thinks
I'm as sweet as honey.

My auntie Ann is as super as Superman
Some people think she might
Not be able to save everyone
But I know she can
So that's my auntie Ann on the go
But there are so many more good things about her
Only I will ever know!

Rochelle Devonport (10)

My Best Friend

My best friend is
Not too low but not too tall,
Not too mean but not too small,
Not too strict but not too cool,
Not too smart but not too dim,
Not too clean but not too grim,
Not too fat but not too slim,
Not too good but not too bad,
Not too sane but not too mad,
Always happy and never sad,
My best friend is . . .
Perfect!

Abigail Markwick (13)

Contrary Cat

My furry friend
Is a contrary cat
He always knows everything that
I am thinking
And lounges around in the sun

If you pick him up
He will wriggle away
If you're eating tea
He will sit on your knee
My black school trousers
That he's never been near
Are covered in bits of gingery hair

His name is Plumpy
He's as thin as a twig
And when he lies out
From his paws to the point of his tail . . .
It goes on and on and on and on and on to
The end.

Freya Ireland (11)

My Dad

My dad is really special,
He likes to play with me.
He takes me to golf
So I can hit a ball off a tee.
We both like trains
And have a track on a table.
He has to help me though,
Until I am able.
My dad's a plumber,
He goes to work in a van
And takes me to work when he can.
My dad is a top man.

Luke Fowler (6)

Can You Guess?

Can you guess what my pet is?
I'll give you a clue,
He's a carrot-eating whizz!

Can you guess the animal in this song?
I'll tell you the truth,
He stays outside all day long.

Can you guess the species of this male?
One cute thing about him is
His fluffy, black tail!

Can you guess the name of this creature?
Fertilising the garden in his worst feature!

Through all his flaws,
We love him so,
Because as far as rabbits go,
He's the best,
He beats the rest,
Our little bunny . . . *Floppy!*

Robyn Gunn (11)

Great Special Someone

You're there for me when I'm down,
When no one else is around.
You make me feel bright like the sun,
You're that great special someone.
You're someone I can talk to,
When I'm sick at home with the flu.
When we're together we have so much fun,
You're that great, special someone.
And what I am saying is true,
And I wish everyone had a great, special someone like you.

Nekeshia McKenzie (11)

My Favourite Person Is My Mum

My mum is my favourite person
She makes me smile
She beats my favourite celeb by a mile.

She cooks me breakfast, lunch and dinner
Isn't that just a winner!

Sometimes she can be a loon
And in other circumstances when she sings she's way out of tune.

She has blue eyes and lovely hair
I think she's pretty and people sometimes stare.

We like walking and going on a wooden swing
And sometimes Mum likes a glass of gin.

Liberty Lee (9)

My Marvellous Mum

My marvellous mum
smiles so bright
My marvellous mum
is such a delight
She cooks
reads books
and says *tut-tut*
and finally says she's had enough
My marvellous mum

My marvellous mum
is always great
My marvellous mum
is never late
She cleans
and dreams
and likes to shout
'Come on,' she says, 'let's have you out!'
but still she is my marvellous mum.

Bethany Jayne May Stannard (10)

My Sister

My sister and I love to go abroad,
My sister has also learned to play a chord.
She is polite
And it is such a sight
To see a child so bright.
She sometimes finds her pencils blunt,
But she's always up for an Easter egg hunt.
My sister loves nature, food too,
She even used to say 'Goo'.
She's nearly nine
And knows how to tell the time.
When she goes to bed,
She always finds it nice to rest her head.

Suzanna Cavadino (6)

My Favourite Person

My grandad is my favourite person and I will tell you why.
He simply is just priceless, there's no money that will buy!
There really isn't a day goes by that we don't have some fun,
And it is especially nice when we are in the sun!

His passion is Man United! The best team in the land!
He also loves his golf (but keep the ball out of the sand!)
He rides his mountain bike and jogs from place to place,
He really is so sporty, I just can't make the pace!

When I hurt my leg he was so kind and warm,
He told me jokes and made me laugh as we sat upon the lawn!
He looks after our hens and keeps their 'palace' clean.
The animals all love him, he really is a dream!

He always has such energy for treats and hugs and laughs.
Where would I be without him? I often think and ask.
He brightens up my day, my life, my every waking hour,
My grandad is my favourite person,
I love him more than the world's power.

Holly Vipond (10)

My Dad

My dad
Is a very special dad
Who can sing and laugh and juggle
His jokes are the best
And his sister is a double
He always gets the right mix
Of firm and love
He's hardly ever strict
He's like a white dove
But the special thing about him, you see
Is that I love him
And he loves me
So we're a happy family.

Brae Parker (9)

My Mum

In 1999 I was born,
I looked up and there
I saw my family staring at me.

In 2002, my first day at nursery.
My mum walked me there.
When I stepped through the gates
I said goodbye to my mum
And toddled into the classroom.

In 2003 I was in primary,
I was a big girl now.
It was further away
But my mum still walked me
Because she cared about me
And I cared about her too.

And now I'm ten and in Year 6,
But guess what?
I still love her now!

Farzana Akhtar (10)

81

Hannah

My favourite person,
Well that's easy,
She's not like a person you see on TV,
She's by me, right next to me,
Every day,
She listens to every single word I say,
No matter what happens,
We will always be together,
Even in the coldest, stormiest weather,
My best friend is the best,
Like no other,
No matter what they say,
We will be friends forever.

Eden Byrne-Young (11)

My Family

I love all my family ever so much,
so instead of writing about just one,
I am writing about them all just to show you how much.

My mum and dad
would do anything for me,
no matter what.

My cousins; Marvin, Ben, Curtis, Ryan, Liam and Jessica,
are there for me till the end.

Aunties and uncles
to love and care.

Grandparents to spoil me
with treats and presents!

Although I write
about what they would do for me,
I would do exactly the same for them,
only ten times more.

Georgia Clarke (11)

I Love My Mum

I love my mum
She is so sweet
She makes good food so tasty to eat

I love my mum
She buys me prezzies
She always lets me play out with my bezzies

I love my mum
She is so soft
She's like a teddy from the loft

I love my mum
And I always will
She just is the bestest thrill.

Nuha Chowdhury (10)

Chloe, The Cat's Day

Chloe gets up off my bed
Stretches in the shape of a shed
In the kitchen she asks for her food
After her breakfast she's always in a very good mood
Then she likes to chase her tail
And ripping up the mail
Afterwards curling up into a tiny ball
Oh my mum's shawl!
Then she goes out
And always likes it when people are about
When she's out she always catches live mice
Which I never find very nice
After her adventure she comes in
And loves to run her head up my shin
Sleeping for nearly the rest of the day
Never forgetting to get up and play
Gobbling up her tea
Then after a while she goes to bed with me.

Stephanie Joy Evans (11)

Ode To Percy

I once had an earwig named Percy,
He was so great, but firstly,
I have to admit that I'm sorry,
When he nearly got squished by a lorry!
And I do hate to remember
That cold day in November,
When the poor little thing
Was flushed down the sink,
(He needed a drink!)
And I cried
When he died.

I still love you Percy,
Held at God's mercy!

Georgia Bartram (11)

Ellis

My favourite person is my nephew Ellis,
He's three and a half weeks old . . .
It only seems like yesterday,
Was the day that I got told . . .

'You're gonna be an uncle,' my mom said,
All I did was smile and my face went red.

I was so excited, I couldn't wait,
But I was a little bit sad 'cause he came out late.

One day, when he gets big,
Me and my nephew can play football and tig . . .

My nephew is someone I'll always cherish,
This is my nephew, my nephew Ellis.

Liam Meah (9)

Mum

Making me happy when I'm upset,
You won't know who that is I bet,
Teaching me how to read,
Grew up just like a little seed,
Also taught me how to write,
Helped to fly my first kite,
Wouldn't trade her for a celeb's life,
Told me not to ever touch a knife,
Took me to nursery when I was four
And then without her it was a bore,
I have to make the most of this time,
Because when I'm older she will be no longer mine,
She built up my personality,
If only she had the power of immortality,
Then she would stay with me forever,
Never leave me never,
By now you must have figured it out,
Mum it's you, it's all about!

Bayan Fadlalla (10)

Peter Andre

Peter Andre is so cool
He likes to swim in his swimming pool
I've heard from his show he likes to party round the clock
And sing non-stop
Peter has a song 'Behind Closed Doors'
It's the song that I adore
Pete's new house is so good
I'd love to live there if I could
I'm Pete's biggest fan
I'd love to tell him if I can
If I was seen with Peter Andre
I would shout, 'Hip, hip, hooray!'
Then we would say what a great day!

Sonnie Smith (11)

My Mum, My Mum, My Mum

My favourite person is my mum
She taught me well so I'm not dumb
My mum makes sure I'm always fine
But also she keeps me in line

My mum, my mum, my mum

I love my mum so very much
She shows me love with every touch
She loves me more and more each day
But doesn't always let me have my own way

My mum, my mum, my mum

My mum always runs around for me
So when she sits down I make her a cup of tea

My mum, my mum, my mum

I love my mum

My mum.

Leah Leonardi (10)

My Favourite Person Is My Teacher

My favourite person is Miss Lowe
She is my teacher and I know
She is always there to give advice
She never shouts and is really nice

She gave me lessons after school
The club she started was really cool
The extra teaching was great fun
She makes me feel as bright as the sun

She let us do some animation
Our cartoon really rocked the nation
She cheered us on as we did sports
That's why she's always in my thoughts.

Jennifer Stokes (10)

Morgan And Me

I have a friend and Morgan's her name,
We met at school and are partners of fame.
'Wind in the Willows' was the name of the play,
What a performance together we made.

We were pupils, nervous and scared,
It took a few days before we settled in there.
We hung around both in a pair,
But up in the classroom we sat at opposite chairs.

I have been to her house, she's been to mine,
Our mums are friends too, we have a great time.

Double trouble, that's who we are,
When we wanna make mischief we don't have to go far.
We usually annoy my brother, her sis,
Having fun is our ultimate bliss!

Time to finish off with a happy ending,
As long as we have each other we will always win!

Maddie Morris (10)

My Favourite Person

My favourite person is one of my sisters,
She looks after us when we're upset,
Has a lovely hamster as a pet,
Loves to know who we've met,
Doesn't really know what we get,
Because she always starts to fret,
Her hair's forever wet,
But she doesn't mind,
She can always bet
There's never gonna be a hairnet.

Abbey Bedford (11)

Tiggy

Tiggy is my cat, the one I love,
The one who gives me lots of hugs.
From where I sit, from where I stand
She will be there lying around.

It's like winter to summer
When she sleeps then wakes,
Sleeps a bit, eats a bit
And she even eats carrot cake.

She hides in the cupboard where no one can find.
She's away with the fairies in her own little mind.

When we go on holiday she stays at my grandparents' house,
Goes in boxes and she would never hurt a mouse.

It's like gazing at the wonders of future life.
You look at the stars and they shine bright.
For the day will come to say a sad goodbye
Flowers where she lies, we will all cry.

Janine Brown (11)

My Little Mouse Chip

He's oh so cute, my special friend,
Little Chip on who I depend.
Always willing to play and learn,
Gives so much and expects nothing in return.

His funny little feet are oh so sweet,
With his bright pink eyes and his pink nose
That glistens like a beautiful rose.
He's always giving, loving and mellow.

This is why I love him so,
I never want to let him go.
This special friend I will love forever,
We will always be together.

Amber Percival (11)

Mum's The Best

1, 2, 3,
She rules,
She rocks,
She loves to shop.

Come on,
She's cool,
She wins,
She always empties the bin!

She makes things that are so yummy,
They always fill my tummy,
She's great to cuddle
And she never gets in a muddle.

How I love my mum,
She is so fun.
She's the best,
Better than all the rest.

Rachel Eager (11)

Untitled

Mummy, Mummy, Mummy
Do you remember when I was in your tummy
Struggling and trying to be free?
After that you saw me
You said, 'What a pretty girl.'
When I wore my pink dress and had a twirl
If I was sad and wasn't happy
You always used to change my nappy
Even, when you were in a bad mood
You still cooked me delicious food.

Amine Nur Dincer (11)

The Legend: Spider-Man

Spider-Man uses his web to soar through the sky
People think it's magic to the eye

As the fierce wind brushes his face
He motionlessly travels from place to place

Quickly he saves people very soon
And concentrates immensely at the wrath of the moon

People thank him with genuine praise
However, there is only one person left to amaze

He's reliant on his instinct and inner-self
Which can dramatically increase his soul and health

A time will come where there is a test
And the obstacles he'll face will be the best of the best.

Shaquille Stephens (11)

Sister

My sister is really funny
She is sometimes a dummy

My sister is really brainy
She drives me crazy

My sister is jolly
She helps Mum push the shopping trolley

My sister is sweet
She always gives me a treat

My sister is the world to me
She always shares her sweets with me

My sister is a friend to me
And she makes me very happy!

Sulaiman Faruqi (8)

My Favourite Person Is . . .

My favourite person is not a person,
But is everywhere I go,
She's with me when I walk around,
In the rain, the wind or snow.

She lets the sun shift through the clouds,
The golden rays upon me.
Melting over tree and town,
An amber world to see.

A silvery river flows down from above,
Given by the stars and moon,
She makes me dream of wonderful things,
But it is gone all too soon.

My favourite person is not a person,
But is everywhere I go.
She's with me when I walk around,
Mother Nature, that I love so.

Laura Dunleavy (11)

Tiger Woods

He is as sharp as a pen nib when he is in the game.
He is a flame of fire when he hits his ball.
He is as slim as an ice lolly.
He is as bold as a boxing glove.
He is as strong as scaffolding on a tall building.
He is as sleek as a cat.
He swings like a monkey swinging from tree to tree.
He is as clever as Einstein.
His smile is as wide as a bridge.
He's as 'posey' as Ronaldo in football.

Tanya Gupta Telukunta (9)

Sisters

Younger and older,
Wherever they are,
They will always be there for you,
Whether they're near or far.

The cuddles, the squabbles,
The pinches, the bites,
The tears of joy,
Followed by tears from fights.

We play, we dance,
We share things together,
The friendship we've got now,
I hope will last forever.

As the years tumble by,
One after another,
I promise you now dear sister,
We will always be there for each other.

Millie Chappell (10)

Clare

Clare is my best friend
She plays with me every day
In the playground with everyone
She is kind to me
And nice to me
She is my one and only true friend
Clare has blonde hair
And brown eyes
She's a great dancer
And the world's greatest friend.

Dearbhail McCaffrey (11)

My Mum Is Just Like The Moon

My mum is my favourite person.

She cooks and cleans, wipes and scrubs
Until the sun goes into the moon.

She gives hugs and kisses all day long
Hard to get away but just when the sun is replaced by the moon
She stops for a minute or two.

She buys and pays all day long
Until the sun is gone.

She's kind and sweet just like the moon
She's good on the inside and good on the outside.

She's the best mum I can think of
Because without her I wouldn't be *me*.

Emma Scott (11)

My Mummy

I love my mummy,
She is so funny,
She makes me laugh
And gives me a bath,
She takes me to places
That are sunny,
Like the park
Where the dogs bark.
We run and have fun
In the sun.

Chase-Lee De'Ath (9)

My Favourite Person

My favourite person is my mum,
You'll know her better when I'm done,
In the summer she sits in the sun
And lets me have water fights, which are lots of fun.

In the autumn, when the leaves are colourful,
My mum is still wonderful.
She always gets me to school on time,
And makes sure I am in bed when the clock says nine.

In the winter, when it's chilly,
She still looks after me, even when I'm silly.
She tucks me into bed at night,
And scares away the ghost that gives me a fright.

In the spring my mummy makes sure
I've got food in my tummy.
I know my mum will always love me,
No matter the reason, or the season.

Timothy MacKenzie (11)

Mum Does Everything

My mum looks like a rose,
My mum smells like a tulip,
My mum tastes like a cookie baked in an oven.
My mum feels like a teddy bear
And she never makes me scared.
When I go to sleep, my mum
Tucks me in nice and deep.
When I wake up,
My mum lets me read a little book.
When I go to school
My mum lets me joke about.
When I finish school
My mum lets me play out with my friends.
My mum is kind and fun.

Chloe Campbell (10)

My Adventurous Pet Dog

I'm a cheeky, tricky pet dog just a sleepy bag of skin,
A sneaky, freaky, fat dog that makes a din,
But sit down on the bean bag and watch the telly with me,
I'll show you some of the greatest dogs that are up my family tree.

Oh I'm no typical lazy dog,
There's something you should know,
I'm as fast as a cheetah,
Just watch me in full flow.

Elvis Bark was a hound dog, playing rock and roll back in '74,
He had some terrific tunes so we all went on a tour.
The crowds who came to see, rocked hard and rolled so sweet,
In our ecstatic frenzy, we all knew this great beat.

Oh I'm no typical lazy dog,
There's something I've forgot,
My claw is as sharp as a sword,
With a hard stone on the top.

Roshni Makwana (12)

My Favourite Person

My favourite person,
Is my ex-head teacher,
From Reception to Year 3,
I have looked up to him,
Always there to escort you a mile ahead,
Always there to encourage you,
Always wants you to succeed,
He loved creative writing,
And when you showed it to him,
Every time he would smile with glee,
He'd get a sticker from his sticker box,
And stick it on my lunch box,
So now you know even though I don't see him,
My favourite person is Mark Shaw.

Iqra Ahmed (12)

My Brother Ollie

Ollie, Ollie, what a lad,
The way he acts and plays is mad,
The Xbox is his favourite thing,
Sometimes he's called the Gaming King.

Call of Duty, FIFA 09,
Whatever game will be just fine,
MSN, Facebook, no one knows,
Whatever he does it always shows.

Beep, beep! Here comes a text,
Out of his bed, shower's next,
But now it's time for the dreaded hairspray,
Which takes hours and hours, but never a day.

Jeans and hoodies, T-shirts too,
Red, green, yellow, even blue,
Down the street with his must have bling,
Headphones in, doing his thing.

Rebecca Smith (12)

Total Blast Gear

My favourite person in the world,
Is someone you might think absurd,
He's not a pop or film star,
He's no one that I know,
This person that I'm speaking of is usually the star of the show,
He guides people through obstacles,
He's never in the rain,
This person that I'm thinking of is sometimes quite insane,
This person is my favourite of all that I know,
He is the best of all the rest and always on the go,
He stars in lots of TV shows,
His nickname it is Hamster,
Got a clue or still in the blue?
His name is Richard Hammond.

Yasmin Boyall (10)

J K Rowling

My favourite person is J K Rowling
The creator of Harry Potter.
Her stories are such marvellous inspiration,
She's just a terrific plotter!

I started her books when I was seven,
But they'll stay with me for life.
They've made me laugh out loud and cry in desperation,
They've made me feel better when going through strife!

Harry and his friends
Are the best characters I'll ever meet,
They're clever, witty and just so funny,
Reading about their adventures is such a treat!

And maybe one day I'll meet J K Rowling
And I'll congratulate her on her success.
I'll tell her how much her stories mean to me
And that she's simply just the best!

Louise Oldham (11)

My Sister Sophia

She's small and pretty
And very witty.
She's funny and kind
And has a clever mind.
She's older than me
Cos she's twenty-three.
But I'm taller and prettier
And much wittier.
I'm funnier and much kinder,
And of that I remind her.
She can go to the pub
And eat all the grub,
But I stay in my den
Because I'm only ten!

Belinda Carini-Nunn (10)

My Younger Brother

My younger brother,
Always alert,
Is also quite happy
To help when you're hurt.

He has wild imagination,
Creating stories for fun,
From bugs to bananas,
He will captivate ev'ryone.

He brings a smile to your face,
He's never felt down,
Always enlightened
(To me he's a clown).

He loves to play with me,
Wherever we are,
He always makes me smile
- It's a permanent memoir.

Ibrahim Sheikh (11)

My Faithful Friend Bruno

He was always there when I was a child
To look over me and protect me.
Every hour of the day and night
He would lie beside my cot keeping an eye on me,
Protecting me like a shepherd does his flock.
Even now I'm older, he still follows me around
As if I was his soul mate.
Every morning the first thing I feel
Is Bruno's soft nose nuzzling into my neck,
Telling me it's time to get up.
Now he's getting older and slower
It's my turn to look after him
And repay the kindness and loyalty
Of my faithful friend Bruno.

Mark Facey (11)

I Don't Know

Two minutes to the start,
The pressure is building up inside him,
Every minute goes by feeling as if an hour has gone past,
The go flag strikes.

He gets three seconds of supreme burn out past the line,
My heart thuds - watching him in anticipation.
He soars down the straight
Like a bullet soaring to the end of its track.

How does he do it?
I don't know,
But he is my idol.

Guess who?
Lewis Hamilton.
But does he even know my name?
I doubt it,
But he is still my favourite person.

Jack Lane (11)

My Grandma

My grandma is the best,
She says, 'You should wear a vest.'
She's very kind,
So keep that in mind.
She's sweet, funny
And likes food in her tummy.
She makes fantastic cakes,
Which are so yummy.
She goes in her car and takes us far
To places we like
And then goes for a hike.
You may not think she's the best,
But to me she'll beat the rest.
My grandma Marie who likes a cup of tea.

Emily Sheppard (10)

Oor Wee Sasha

Oor wee Sasha is a wee smasher
With her full set of nashers
Daredevil Sasha, who thinks she's a chancer
Give her curry crisps and she'll show she's a dancer.

Oor wee Sasha is a wee poser
Take her anywhere and everybody knows her
She stands on the frozen pond as if she's a skater
She can dig bricks as if she's a slater.

Oor wee Sasha is a wee horror
She munchies and crunchies and hopes no one saw her
Sasha likes her sweets to eat
And lies like lady muck on the three piece suite.

Oor wee Sasha is a wee nuisance
Playing about with my mammy's new cushions
Pulling her toys out she thinks she's a sinner
But give her, her dinner and she knows she's a winner.

Jordon Anderson (8)

I Remember

(In loving memory of Fiona Hitchcock, loving Mum. RIP)

I remember her deep brown eyes,
The crazy hair, the big warm smile,
Applying her Lipsyl wherever she goes,
With her family around her, she had a brilliant lifestyle.

As I think of that smile,
Which spread across her face,
I would travel so far to see her,
Just to be there in her embrace.

She was kind, loyal and loving,
I still feel she's nearby,
I know she'd want me to be happy,
But it hasn't been long since the last goodbye.

Elizabeth Hitchcock (12)

My Little Sister

My favourite ever person
is always really happy.
She's had a big smile on her face
since she was in her nappy.

My favourite ever person
has lovely dark brown hair.
It floats below her shoulders
but sometimes sticks out in the air.

My favourite ever person
is always kind and sweet.
She'd never make you cry
unlike my dad's stinky feet!

If you're feeling really sad
she will make it better.
My favourite ever person
is my lovely sister Becca!

Bethany Nash (10)

My Best Friend

My best friend is Dayna,
She is very cool,
We are both starting something new,
Secondary school.

We have mixed feelings,
We don't know how to feel,
It will be an adventure,
In our minds very unreal.

But we're going to different places,
With new classrooms,
With new faces,
We will still be best friends,
Our friendship will never end.

Laura Hutchinson (11)

Untitled

My cousin is my favourite person,
She is as funny as can be.
A million things she teaches me,
Even how to make tea.

When things go wrong, she will always be there,
To help and put things right.
She does so many activities with me,
And she can never lose my sight!

With her around everything is great,
She can teach you right from wrong.
The only disadvantage she has is . . .
Her socks really do pong!

Our closest feelings for each other,
Are entwined.
A better and greater cousin,
I could never ever find!

Henna Pratik Patel (11)

My Yummy Mummy!

I have lots of relations
Friends and family
But there's one person who fills my heart with joy
We get along so happily

She buys me presents and surprises me with treats
She gave birth to my sister who is very sweet
She taught me how to dance and sing
She taught me almost everything

She watches me and helps me too
She believes in everything I do
She cooks delicious food for my tummy
Have you guessed? Yes, it's my mummy!

Sruti Saraswatula (8)

Molly . . . ?

Molly is my very best friend,
Although she might not be
Pretty to anyone else,
She's perfect enough for me.

I've known her for as long as I can remember
And she's still with me today,
We have an extra special bond together
And we use it when we play.

She's different, she's special, she makes me smile,
After all, she's just like you and me.
Each and every time I see her
She fills me up with glee.

I never go anywhere without her,
We always stick together.
Precious Molly is my rag doll,
She'll stay with me forever.

Nieve Walton-O'Brien (10)

My Favourite Person? Renata

Renata is my friend,
She is cute and sweet,
I really like her,
As if her heart had a beat.

Renata is my friend,
She is a really great girl,
I wonder who bullies her,
In a great twirl.

I like Renata,
She is the best,
I guess no one can beat her,
In this competition test.

Eddy Oliveira (10)

Duchess The Rabbit

I lost her when I was only eleven,
Now she is on her way up to Heaven.
How she used to smile at me
When I sat there and watched her pee.

I can't believe we had to part,
I will always love her with all my heart.
I loved it when she hopped.
It made me sad when she stopped.

My rabbit and I,
We thought we could fly.
Now she has gone so far.
She was my number one star.

I loved her soft black and white coat,
But I didn't when it got down my throat.
She will always be my best friend.
Forever, till the end.

Shauna Green (11)

My Grandad

I was devastated when he died
And now I sit here and cry and cry.
I know he's happy up in Heaven,
But I wish he was here down in Devon.

Through the happy times and the sad,
He was never really bad.
In my heart he is alive
And in my heart he will survive.

Always, from the start
He's never out of my heart.
He will never, ever fade away,
Because he's my grandad and he *will* stay.

Leigh-Anne Preston (11)

My Mum

My mum is the greatest,
I love her all the way,
She plays with me and cares for me,
Every single day.

My mum is very caring,
And kind and patient too.
She helps me and supports me,
In everything I do.

My mum understands me,
No one can beat that.
Whenever I am feeling down,
She gives me a good pat.

My mum is so special,
She's better than the rest.
I love my mum with all my heart,
My mum is really the best.

Amy Young (11)

My Favourite Person Is Ollie

Ollie is a hamster
He lives in my house
I love him so much
He looks like a mouse.

I loved Freddy as much as Ollie
But sadly he died
I was crying on the way home from school
But Ollie is still alive.

He runs in his ball
When Daddy changes him
He has got to stay in the living room
Of the house we live in.

Emily Maloney (6)

Peter

My tennis coach Peter
Is the best
You can get
We rally, we run
We break into a sweat
He makes me happy
And brings out my skills
It's really hard
It's like running up hills
When I want to give up
He cheers me on
I just have to go on
He makes me strong
He is the best ever coach
I really like his volley
Thanks to you Peter
You make me jolly.

Jaidyn Dilon Murray (10)

My Best Mate!

We are best friends,
You and me,
Together forever, just wait and see.
Both blonde and blue-eyed,
Active and filled with glee,
It's not our fault that we will always be,
One smaller, the other taller,
We scare each other
Like good friends do,
Then we definitely need to go to the loo.
Best mates always.

Brogan Pickering (11)

My Favourite Person

My favourite person is my dad,
Because he is funny, handsome,
Smart and a bit mad
(In a good way)
You would think of him as a nice man
But to me he means the whole world.
He is unique and different from any other person.
He is such a nice man, he'll make you smile.
The way he talks, the way he walks,
I love him in every way,
Because he is my dad.

Nazifa Ibrahim (11)

Terrific Terry, My Best Friend

Terry, Terry, wild and contrary
Is my favourite friend
But sometimes when we laugh and play
He drives me round the bend
We often play together
Being soldiers and Russian spies
We tell each other secrets
But never ever lies.

We play around each other's house
Making lots of noise
Sometimes playing with his pet mouse
Mostly with our toys
Always driving our mums mad
But look at what fun we had!

Tony Colvin (10)

My Brother Niall

My brother plays the drums,
But it's better than messing with guns!
All he can think about is his hair,
If it's not right it gives him a scare.
My brother is so lazy,
But he's definitely not crazy!
He never takes off his hat
And is really not that fat!
He is a kebab and pizza king,
Even though he has no gold ring.
He winds me up and makes me shout
And often leaves his clothes about!
But all this aside,
He fills me with pride,
At the end of the day,
He's my brother and I
    Love him!

Finnlay Walsh (10)

The Fastest Man Alive

On your marks, get set, *bang!*
Usain flies out of his blocks,
The sprinting world was about to be rocked.
In Berlin at the World Championship
The world record he was to blitz.
'Go slower,' the other competitors beg.
Usain Bolt the fastest man on two legs.
Usain you are greater than great.
A new world 100 metres record in 9.58.
This incredible athlete you cannot fault,
He is of course, the legendary Usain Bolt.

Marc Piper (11)

Marvellous Mum

My favourite person is my mum,
she is loving, friendly, kind and *fun.*
She cares for me all day long,
and really never gets things wrong.
My mum is the best, she tidies the house,
not a peep of dust or even a mouse,
is allowed to settle in our home,
otherwise, she will shout and moan.
My mum does the ironing, cleaning and the dishes,
she's like Cinderella but without the wishes . . .
I love my mum, she is the best and I'm sure she will beat the rest!

Sophie Goodenough (10)

A Friendly Face

My favourite person always:
Makes me smile when I'm about to cry
Makes me remember I never have to say goodbye
I can tell her all my secrets and know she can keep them close
As she is the one I can trust the most
My favourite person always:
Gives me the best time of my life.

We always exchange our favourite hats,
Because that's just the way we act
We love to sing our favourite riddles, like Hey Diddle Diddle
Who is my favourite person?
A person so close to me since the day I was born
A person who I can trust and is always there for me
My favourite person is my mum.

Lucy Mackintosh (11)

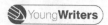

My Favourite Person

She's kind,
She's caring,
She's funny,
She's smart,
She's lovely,
She's cool.
All these things are true I swear!
Ask her if you don't believe me!
She's my friend,
Oh yes she is!
She's just like me,
We are practically sisters!
We always get along!
We will always be friends,
More than friends,
More than best friends,
We will always be sisters!

Natasha Smith (9)

A Dedication To My Mother

To the one who's smart and not insane
Who's beautiful without being vain
Who shares my joys in happiness
Who wipes my tears in sadness

She laughs with me when I laugh
She comforts me when I cry
She will always be there for me
Through the lows and the highs

I rely on her, depend on her
And will always be a friend to her
I'll pray for her as there is no other
Who will ever replace my truly amazing mother!

Mother I love you.

Sidra Zainab (10)

110

My Favourite Person

My favourite person is the one
Who isn't shy, who is brave.
My favourite person is a friend
Not an enemy.
My favourite person is someone
Who's nice, not someone who's mean.
My favourite person is someone
Who respects my feelings and doesn't hurt them.
My favourite person is someone
Who listens to me instead of ignoring me.
My favourite person is somebody
Who trusts me and doesn't laugh at my secrets.
My favourite person is someone
Who likes me, but doesn't hate me.
My favourite person is someone
Who cheers me up when I'm upset.
My favourite person is my *mum!*

Larissa Aravantinou (10)

My Best Friend

My best friend is my dog,
she is the best of all.
I love her very much,
and her favourite toy is a ball.

She loves to pounce,
bounce and leap.
But most of all she likes her sleep.

My dog Jessie is the best
she stands out from all the rest.
She wears a hoodie to make her tough,
when she sees people she goes, 'Woof!'

My friends at school think she's cool,
but my dog Jessie really rules.

Kaitlyn Templeman (10)

Once Upon A Time

Here as I watch the moon light up the sky,
I'm singing this sleepy lullaby.
Once upon a time,
I thought everything was fine,
but boy was I wrong, to sing that song,
where you and I fall in love.
Later that time,
I wished upon a star
and promised thee that you would be mine.
Once upon a time,
I believed in fairytale love
and believed in love's first kiss,
that's what I miss.
Once upon a time,
I too, believed in love at first sight.
Now I will never fall for the wrong,
I must fall for the right.

Nora Berzina (10)

My Mummy

My mummy is the best,
Definitely better than all the rest!
My life is never dull,
And my tummy is always full!

I love my mummy very much,
She always gives that special touch!
Whenever I am feeling down,
She turns my smile the right way round!

That is why,
She is my
Favourite person!

I'll love her forever,
And we'll always be together!

Elizabeth Drinkwater (10)

JLS!

JLS are cool
JLS are fun
I know they mess about sometimes
But I still think they're number one.
There's Marvin, Aston, Oritsé and JB,
I think they're funny and like JD.
They have a new album, I think it's really good,
They could have had a chance of winning X Factor
But their luck was no good.
I love 'Beat Again' and also 'Umbrella',
They have lots of movement,
I think it's really clever.
There are four lads
That aren't bad.
They like the colours, red, green, yellow and blue,
They definitely don't moo!
They're tellin' me that my heart won't beat again!

Reshmi Jay Patel (10)

My Mum

My mum, she's the best,
She never has a rest.
She works here, there, everywhere
And is always there for us!

My mum, she's great,
She never has a break.
If Mum sees that I'm upset,
She'll hug me for what seems like hours.

I love my mum,
She's lots of fun.
She knows what's best
And is most tre-men-dous!

I love you Mum!

Hannah Berry (11)

My Favourite Person Is . . .

Someone who cares about me.
Someone who shelters me.
Someone who loves me.
Someone who will go to the bottom of the Earth,
Just to find out what I want.

Someone who buys me clothes.
Someone who wants the best for me.
Someone who buys me food.
Someone who will do the weirdest things
Just to know I am safe.

Someone who will die for me.
Someone who protects me.
Someone who supports me,
Even if I've done bad.
Someone who will give me a great childhood.
My favourite person is my mum.

Alexander Wellington (10)

Elise

She always has a smile
Which is worthwhile
She always makes me laugh
Even in the bath

She always is kind
And speaks her mind
She always is fun
But she hates to run

She always cares
Especially for cuddly bears
She always loves
And gives winter gloves.

We are best friends forever.

Hetty Bostock (10)

My Favourite Person

My favourite person is my sister,
When she goes away I always miss her,
I love my sister.

She can't walk, so has a set of wheels,
Her favourite things are her meals,
I love my sister.

We always laugh and play,
Seeing her smile makes my day,
I love my sister.

My sister is very pretty,
If she could talk, I'm sure she'd be witty,
I love my sister.

My sister is my best friend,
I hope our love will never end,
I *love* my sister!

Francesca Riley (10)

My Favourite Person

I wake up in the morning and I see a smile,
I go into the bathroom and I see the smile again,
I have breakfast and I see the smile again,
I get ready for school and see the smile again,
I say goodbye . . .
I come home from school and I see the smile again,
I go to the mosque and the smile is there again,
I come home from the mosque and I see the smile again,
I go to bed and I see the smile again,
The smile that was with me all day was my favourite person . . .
My mum.

Junaid Saddique (9)

My Best Friend

My best friend is my favourite person
She is always there for me
And her name is Georgia Leigh!

My best friend is absolutely great
She is better, better than the rest
My best mate!

We've had some great times together
From sleepovers to makeovers
Me and my best friend forever!

She will always be there for me
I will always be there for her
Waiting for new adventures to occur!

That's my best friend, so keep your hands off!

Kelsey Brigden (11)

My Baby Brother

My baby brother likes not to share
screaming and shouting, he doesn't care

My baby brother is too active
likes to be so attractive

My baby brother likes his fashion
it is a passion

My baby brother acts wild
and says he's a big child

My baby brother is a non-night sleeper
and a full-time leaper

My baby brother is a Toys R Us fan
and a great little man

Some people think he's just a part of the crowd
but he's my favourite person and that's why I'm proud!

Bayse Genc (10)

My Favourite Person

I have a favourite person, his name is Jeff Hardy,
WWE wrestling superstar,
He amazes me with his high-flying moves,
But sometimes he can go a bit too far.
His signature moves are the swan-ton bomb,
Whisper in the wind and the awesome twist of fate.
He performs in the ring alone or sometimes with Matt,
His brother and best mate.

Jeff's true wrestling rival is a dude named CM Punk,
His dream is to demolish Jeff Hardy,
But rumour has it he reeks like a smelly old skunk!

When I'm older I'd like to be a star just like Jeff,
Entertaining with my signature moves
And fancy flips that might just take your breath!

Reece Boulton (10)

My Furry Friend

She wakes me up in the morning,
When I am very sleepy,
She's always there for me,
When I am very weepy.
With her soft and silky black fur
And her jet-black paws,
Her bushy tail and bright orange eyes.
She's my very best friend!
Have you guessed yet?
I'll make a bet,
It's Saskia, my cat!

Danielle Jones (11)

Me And My Collie Friend Rex

We play all day,
Afterwards he likes to lay.

We take him for a walk,
Meanwhile we also talk.

We also go for lots of runs,
During which we have lots of fun.

We laugh and play,
And Rex runs along the way.

He enjoys to play with something thick,
It normally is a big fat stick.

We have had so much fun,
And I am sure there is loads more to come.

Rex is my best friend,
And I hope our friendship will never end.

Hannah Greenwood (9)

My Favourite Person

My favourite person is Alice
I don't talk to her with malice
She has long hair which is very fair
My favourite person is Alice
We have lots of sleepovers together
Each time it gets a lot better
We muck about and then help out
My favourite person is Alice
We go to the cinema in a very fancy car
We play lots of games like races and skipping
Nothing will stop me and Alice.

Emily Longhurst (8)

Untitled

My friend is amazing and if you met her you would see,
That if ever I was lonely, she'd always be there for me!
One day when it was raining, black and grey was the colour of the sky,
She came along with a smiley face and lifted my spirits high.
If ever I ask her to come with me shopping, she'll say,
                                        'Yeah, course, that's fine!'
'10.00 sharp,' I'd say and she'd always be there on time.

Hannah is also very creative, an artist she could be,
And when she shows me all of her work, a pleasure it is to see.
She is very kind and loving and absolutely incredible,
She really, really, really deserves a best ever friend gold medal!

My friend is amazing and now you'll probably see,
That whenever I am lonely, she'll always be here for me.
Now I see how lucky I am for her to be best friends with me!

Katherine Fallows (10)

Untitled

Dean Ashton is the very best
Better than all the rest
Scoring hat-tricks for West Ham
And I'm his number one fan
Watching him on the TV
Making my smile full of glee
Because I like him so very much
If he wants me to I'll even learn Dutch
Just seeing him makes me smile
Watching him is worth my while
So I'm his number one fan!

Harrison Mills (9)

My Family

My favourite person is . . .

Is it my mom? She takes me to school
and I think she's really cool.

Is it my dad? He built our house
and to cheer me up he acts like a mouse.

Is it my sister Laura Jane?
Sometimes she shouts and hurts my brain!

Is it my brother Benjamin?
We play on our Nintendos and I always win.

Or is it my dog? Her name is Belle.
We take her for walks and she's as fast as hell.

I could not choose between either one
Belle, Ben, Laura, Dad or Mom,
They are my favourite people.

Hannah Moore (8)

My Favourite Person

My favourite person makes me laugh,
She sings in the shower and the bath.
She's great at piano and PE,
She begs my mum to buy a Wii.

Her room is always in a mess,
She likes the egg, but not the cress.
The fact she can chat for hours,
Proves that she has super powers.

I really do like her a lot,
Thanks to the qualities she's got.
Like loving a good tongue twister,
I can't help it, she's my sister.

Guanhong Li (11)

My Favourite Person 2009

My favourite person is cool and funny, loyal to her friends.
She loves listening to music but what mood she is in it depends.

Her favourite food is watermelon, chocolate and crème brulee.
She loves dancing, watching all the videos on TV every day.

Speaking of TVs, she loves all the soaps,
When anything goes wrong, she has the strength to cope.

My favourite person loves shopping, bags and accessories and the rest.
Even though she loves shopping, athletics is the best.

She loves to go on the computer, talking to everyone on MSN,
Also she likes to make on the farm, a good den.

She has lots of pets, all kinds of animals, dogs, cats, chickens and doves,
But when it comes to mucking out she has to wear gloves.

I hope you have guessed who my favourite person is,
Well. I have, it is *me!*

Bethany Marshall (11)

My Cousin

Her name is Maya,
She can be a liar,
But she's really clever,
She's always on fire.

She's a cousin who talks,
She's a cousin who listens,
She's a cousin who fights,
And a cousin who's smitten.

She loves to colour,
She loves to bake food,
She loves her mother
And her favourite word is 'dude'.

Simran Seehra (11)

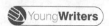

My Sister Sophie

M essy
Y ounger

S weet
I ntelligent
S pontaneous
T all
E ight
R unner

S illy
O pen-minded
P retty
H ilarious
I nquisitive
E ager

And that's my sister Sophie!

Emily-Frances Allen (11)

My Favourite Person

My mum's cool, my mum's fun
My mum's really number one
She loves Chinese and Indian food
She never tells me what to do
She's jolly kind, indescribable words
My mum makes me proud of her
With lots of hugs and lots of kisses
Buddies together, we can do so much
She's a bursting bubble of beauty with brown eyes
And hair as soft as a fluffy cushion
My mum's my favourite person because she cares.

Herjyot Manku (10)

My Mad Dad!

My dad may not have much hair,
but I like it when he pretends to be the big bear.

My dad likes going for a pint,
but I like him best when he's the big giant.

He also turns into Mosquito Man,
he bites people on the bum,
especially my brother Sam.

He turns into so many people,
pretends to be a beggar under a church steeple.

He has lots of accents like Indian or French,
and sometimes sleeps on an old park bench.

My dad likes to be somebody else,
but I love him best when he's just himself.

Carla Nevin (8)

The Only One I Trust

I once said 'trust no one' until I met the one
With the same name as me . . . Katie.
She told me secrets which the friends she's known longer don't know.

I tell her things that most people would give me a weird look for.
I know that everything she says is the truth
And she knows she can trust me.

Katie always knows what and how I feel -
She looks out for me but doesn't smother me.

We are the cherries on each other's cakes,
She is my source of happiness,
I am her source of laughter.

But the strangest is . . . we met each other . . .
On the Internet.

But that doesn't stop me trusting.

Katie Knowles (11)

My Teacher's The Best

Mrs McCutcheon's so fine,
Mrs McCutcheon's so great,
She puts everyone in a line,
She helps us count to 108.

Mrs McCutcheon's so fab,
Mrs McCutcheon's so funny,
It's as if we work in a clown lab,
She makes our lives so sunny!

Mrs McCutcheon's so magnificent,
Mrs McCutcheon's so brilliant,
Spending our education time with her
Turns our lives around.

That's why my teacher is
My favourite person.

Heather Wickens (11)

My Idol Beyoncé

Beyoncé Knowles is my inspiration,
For her I have much adoration,
She is so natural and so sweet,
Listening to her is a real treat,
She sings her heart out every day,
She makes me happy in every way,
She takes up her time giving great advice,
And helping people live their lives,
She keeps good care of her health,
And tells many people about herself,
She also knows how to multitask,
When she's not singing her acting's top class,
She's really kind and really cares,
I really like the clothes she wears,
Because of the things she does and says,
She's stayed my role model today!

Emma Davey (12)

My Favourite Person: Marianne

(Dedicated to my big sister Marianne!)

Marianne is my sister,
I love her to bits.
She's so funny,
She has me in laughing fits.
Her hair's brunette,
Her eyes dazzling blue.
I love her so much
And she loves me too.
Marianne's 24,
Never a bore.
Creative and helpful,
Not one day is dull,
Because Marianne is smart, funny
And beautiful!

Antonia Day (11)

My Big Brother Alex

My big brother Alex is my special chum,
He makes me laugh until it hurts my tum.
He's big and tall, strong and kind,
When I borrow his things, he doesn't mind.
We like to play badminton and ride our bikes,
Race on the PlayStation and go on hikes.
When I was little he helped me a lot,
First when I was a baby, then a tot.
Sometimes we disagree and have a fight,
But never go to bed without making it right.
He's very clever and knows a lot about cars,
And very fair when sharing chocolate bars.
He loves to joke and is actually very witty,
When I feel down, he tells me I'm pretty,
I'm so lucky to have my big brother Al,
As long as I live, he will be my best pal.

Isabelle Jackson (10)

Buddy!

Buddy is my puppy
Buddy is my best friend ever
He is nice and fluffy
He likes to eat snow
He likes to watch me bubble-blow
Buddy is my best friend ever
But I really think he is not very clever

When he does his doggy eyes
You know he has left you a little surprise
He chews on my underwear
They were all the way over there!
He likes pairs of socks
More than his doggy chocs!
He likes to roll in the mud
But all I say is . . . that's my Bud!

Hannah Gowen (9)

My Mum Rocks

M y mum means so much to me
Y es, so much, I wish I had three

M y mum takes me out and we have so much fun
U ndeniably *fab,* that's my mum
M aking me smile, such a big grin

R eally, so much, it hurts my chin
O n my birthday she spoils me
C hristmases too, and my family
K nowing she's there every day
S he rocks my life in every way.

Emma Howes (9)

Who Is My Favourite Person?

Well, maybe it's my mum, fantastic and funny,
'Cause she's loved me since I was in her tummy!
Maybe it's my dad, Stoke's number one fan,
Going to work in his noisy red van!
Perhaps it's my sister or even my brother,
And they annoy everyone, not just each other!
Maybe it's my grandad or maybe my nan,
Playing in the park whenever we can!
Perhaps it was my last teacher at St Gregory's Primary School,
Even though we had lots of work, I had plenty of good times too!
Maybe it's my best friend, who always makes me smile,
Staying over at her house, laughing all the while!
Maybe it's Edward Cullen AKA Robert Pattinson,
I am Twilight's biggest fan and he is number one!
Who is my favourite person? Who could it possibly be?
Well I think my favourite person is no one other than me!

Lauren Grattage (11)

Superstar!

Who makes me smile?
You do!
Who loves me all the while?
You do!
Who always knows what to say?
You do!
Who brightens up every day?
You do!
Who makes my troubles disappear!
You do!
Who always has no fear?
You do!
Who is always my special friend?
You are:
My mum, my number one *superstar!*

Bethany-Mae Jones (10)

Now He Has Gone

Jeff Hardy was in the WWE,
whisper in the winds, Swanton bombs,
they all amazed me, after nine years of watching him in the ring,
one night on Smackdown,
C M Punk came along,
he challenged him to a fight,
a fight that if Jeff lost he
would be gone for a very long time,
it was intense, they both fought their best,
but in the closing moments, it was C M Punk who came out on top, as Jeff lay
there in the middle of the ring, everyone was crying,
everyone didn't want to see Jeff lose,
after he got up, he said his goodbye forever,
I wish he had won,
hopefully I will see him again sometime soon,
that is why Jeff is my favourite person ever.

George Lucas (13)

My Favourite Person

My favourite person is a spaceman,
He takes me on his rocket ship,
We also go to galaxies,
Where nobody's even heard of it!
My favourite person is a pirate,
He takes me on his pirate boat,
We fire our canons as we
Look for our treasure that can float!
My favourite person is a singer,
I help her practise her show,
We always dance whenever or wherever,
She reminds me of Marilyn Monroe!
I don't really know who to choose,
I think my whole family are my favourite,
Because together we never lose!

Kayleigh Corbet-Adams (11)

Joe Jonas

Joe Jonas is the star I love,
I wish he'd fall down from the sky above!
We have a lot in common,
that's why I think we'll get on.
We've got the same sign,
his birthday is the day after mine.
He's incredibly funny,
making me a happy bunny!
His favourite colour is blue,
yum, uh oh, I think I'm going cuckoo.
I love his music and brothers,
just wish they were my lovers.
Kevin, Nick and Frankie,
OMG I think I need a hanky!
I will love Joe Jonas forever and ever,
I won't stop loving him I tell you, never, ever, ever!

Cerys McGivern (11)

My Dad!

My dad cheers me up when I'm down,
he never likes an unhappy frown.
He likes to play and work all day,
but that's my dad!

Is he like your dad?
Hopefully not!
My dad is totally unique.
It's my dad!

He's not the same,
hates seeing people get the blame.
He is my dad,
that's what makes me proud to call him *mine!*

Lauryn Douglas Hayward (11)

Wonderful Sis!

Hayley is my older sister,
We get on like a poodle and a blister,
Even though we fight all the time,
I'm glad she's the sister I can call mine.
12 years of my life, with her in tow,
She can be quite annoying, don't you know.
I love her whether she's mean or nice,
But she's certainly no sugar and spice.
Family ties and sibling fun,
Sometimes we connect as one.
We love each other no matter what,
She's the only sister that I've got.
Whether we're out at the movies,
Or dancing at the groovies,
She will always be,
My wonderful sis!

Stuart Boyce (12)

Peter Crouch

He's big,
He's red,
His feet hang out of the bed,
It's Peter Crouch, it's Peter Crouch!

He's big,
He's tall,
He's always on the ball,
It's Peter Crouch, it's Peter Crouch!

He's big,
He's tough,
He always does good stuff,
It's Peter Crouch, it's Peter Crouch!

Sonia Puri (11)

People Searching

My favourite person, hmmm that's tricky
I'm going to find out the answer but I am quite picky
Maybe it's a footballer like Beckham or Owen
To find out the answer I better get goin'
Maybe a band like Take That or Westlife
If not someone's famous wife
Cheryl Cole or Mrs Claus
A cartoon character with paws
Tom, Jerry, Scooby-Doo
Even Tigger, Piglet and Pooh
What about Paris, Posh or Brown
The Queen, JK or Krusty the Clown
Someone in the family? Mum, Dad or maybe me
But wait now I see
My favourite person is . . .
Neil Buchanan from Art Attack.

Dana Leslie (11)

My Little Sister

I have this little sister,
She makes me really glad,
I have someone to talk to,
But sometimes she makes me mad.

She is always there for me,
Every night and day,
I love her to bits,
Though sometimes forget to say.

I love her more than ever,
I just want her to hear,
She is my little sister,
I'll always hold her near.

Tolia Uwalaka (10)

My Dog

My dog Buffy is a little toughy,
he is cute and very fluffy.
He bites the washing off the line,
but I don't get there in time.
He is so very cute
and loves to play with his toy boot.
Can't believe eight months have gone,
my little Buffy is growing big and strong.
When he goes to the vets,
he plays with other people's pets.
When I go to school he cries.
So when I go and I say to him,
'Don't worry I'll be back in a mo.'
A dog is not just for Christmas
but it is for life, oh yes, it's very true,
in fact I love my Buffy, I really, really do!

Elena Napoliello (9)

My Favourite Person Is My Mum

My mum is caring.
My mum helps me when I am upset.
My mum cuddles me day and night.
My mum is one of a kind!

My mum takes me to school.
My mum helps me with my homework.
My mum lets me have friends over.
My mum is one of a kind!

My mum takes me to the park.
My mum takes me to clubs.
My mum helps me build my confidence.
My mum is the best in the world!

Caroline Richardson (10)

She's Great!

My favourite person is somewhat different,
She's not always understood and
Sometimes struggles to understand why.
Yet it doesn't hold her back, as it is not an illness,
But part of everyday life!

She's my sister and she was born deaf in both ears,
We don't treat her any differently
And nor do we expect anyone else to.
She's now twelve and coping just fine,
I'm proud of her, in fact, we all are!

As I said, my favourite person is somewhat different,
She's not always understood and
Sometimes struggles to understand why.
Yet it doesn't hold her back, as it is not an illness,
But a part of every . . . day . . . life!

Chelsea Williams (11)

Luana

My first dog,
Loved to jog.
She loved to lick,
My sandals were her favourite things to nick.
She was my favourite pet,
My family were the only people she met.

But one day I had to say goodbye,
As I cried while time flew by.
So I'll never forget,
My wonderful pet, Luana.

Joana Carvalho

My Little Brother

My little brother is a star,
He'd love to drive a car.

He is so tall,
But he loves football.

Yet he likes rice
And hates mice.

If you give him water
He'll drink a quarter.

He'll play a drum
And he is never glum.

After rice he will eat naan
And his name is Eesa Khan.

But still he's my little bro.

Hamza Khan (9)

My Best Dad Ever

My dad is the best,
He is better than the rest.
My dad is clever,
He is the best dad ever.
At times he's funny
And sometimes gives me money.
My dad is sporty
And never naughty.
All the time he's caring
And always sharing.

Safia Mahmood (8)

My Parents

My mum and dad
Watched me being born
At twenty-six weeks old
'There's not much chance
He'll make it,'
From the doctors they were told.

They couldn't eat,
They couldn't sleep,
They prayed in every way,
And God must have been listening
Because I'm still here today.

I'm four foot tall and weigh six stone,
No more two pounds for me,
It's all down to the love and care
My parents gave to me.

Jordan Eyre (10)

Me And My Four-Legged Friends

We go to the park, all they do is bark.
We go to play tag and their tails always wag.
I throw them sticks and they give me licks,
They give me paw when they want more.
We run and play for most of the day,
There's Harvey and Lottie and Alfie and me.
Now we are all going home to have our tea.
Now our bellies are full and our day is done,
We all settle down and don't make a sound.
Zzzzzz.

Ellie McIntyre (11)

Number One Nan

My nan is . . .

Sweet and kind
but she's half-blind

She may be old
but she's certainly not bold

She gives me some money
and she really is funny

I give her all my trust
by the way she likes to eat the crust

I love her
but she might have some blubber

Man
it's my number one nan.

Harley Jones (10)

Why You Make Me Smile

Why do I smile when you're around?
Why do I frown when you are down?
Why do I cry when you are sad?
Why do I listen when you are mad?
You're my best friend ever,
Even when you're at the end of your tether!
There's nothing I wouldn't do for you at times,
Including making up this rhyme!
So now I ask why you make me smile
And that's because you're number 1 in my eye!

Krista Armstrong (13)

Mum

(I would like to dedicate this poem to my wonderful mum who has helped me through tough times and she's so special that I cannot think of anything good enough to give her back as a present apart from my love.)

I'm looking in the mirror
And I think I'm liking what I see
Your smiling face
Smiling brightly at me.

I'm looking at the bright blue sky
And I think I'm liking what I see
A cloud shaped like you
With your arm around me.

I'm looking at the sky at night
And I think I'm liking what I see
Shimmering stars that represent the beautiful bond
Between you and me!

Aoife Cassidy (10)

Jenny

My best friend is Jenny,
The lovely Jersey calf,
She walks with me on a halter
And runs around and makes me laugh.

Her coat is smooth and shiny,
She has beautiful big brown eyes,
And at the county shows,
She always wins a prize.

But she's growing really fast now,
And eats all the food she sees,
So soon she'll have her own little calf,
And provide us with milk and cheese.

Lucy Reeve (8)

My Granny Rocks!

M y favourite person in the world has got to be my granny,
Y ou wouldn't believe the laughs we have, she's always
   very funny.

G orgeous and great, she knows how to groove -
R eady to sing with the ABBA moves!
A lways baking scrumptious food,
N ow we're in a brilliant mood!
N ew sparkling outfits that are dazzling - no doubt,
Y early shows in London - Grease was a great trip out.

R eady to sew on hundreds of sequins,
O pening the treat cupboard, giving us Penguins!
C old walks with the dogs, watching them bound!
K eeping your secrets nicely safe and sound.
S aying the things I love about my granny makes me
   and her very, very happy!

Emma Danielle Claxton (11)

My Mum Is Fun

Whenever I am feeling scared,
Whenever I am sad,
My mum will always cheer me up,
She goes completely mad!

She sneaks me up some chocolate,
She takes me out for treats
And before my grumpy dad gets back,
She makes sure my room is neat!

I really love my mum a lot,
She is my all-time best friend
And even when we occasionally argue,
We quickly make amends.

Florence Howard (11)

My Best Mates

My best mates are calm, cool and collected,
we have adventures here and there,
known as *The Trio* everywhere.

Our adventures are astounding,
talked about all over the playground,
and the treasure we have found.

Once in our library we discovered an ancient treasure map,
the book had a secret flap.

We followed the riddle around the playground,
until we found a chest at the bottom of a tree,
inside was a musty, dusty scroll that said,
'Adventure with friends is the true treasure
and it will last forever'.

And, to this very day, that has remained true.

Alex Moreland (11)

Poppy Poem

You'll have to meet Poppy,
She's really rather sweet,
But very, very fussy,
About the food she'll eat.

She lives in my garden,
In a rather cosy hutch,
I don't think she liked
The indoor one that much.

But if you hold some broccoli up
She'll really have to grab it.
I think you've probably guessed by now
That Poppy is a *rabbit!*

Emily Denny (11)

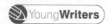

My One And Only Mum

My mum is always there for me
Never backing down,
It doesn't matter what else is going on,
Or if there's smiles, even worse, a frown.

Because my mum's always there for me
Picking up the pieces,
And I hope she will still love me
Until I have grandchildren and nieces.

No one is more special to me
Than my one and only mum,
That is why I am writing you this poem,
Because she truly deserves my everlasting love.

Alana Stevenson (10)

My Favourite Papa

My favourite person rocks,
He is so cool,
I love him everywhere,
Even in the pool.

He loves playing golf
With all his mates,
And watching cricket.
Misbehaviour he hates.

He is an eye doctor,
So marvellous is he,
But . . . best of all,
He loves me!

Laurie Reznik (10)

Mother's Kindness

My mother always helps me
When I'm always stuck
She helps me with my homework
And always gives me luck

My mother never lets me down
When I'm in the blues
I can always count on her
Whatever day I choose

My mother is a trusting friend
Who is always there
I will always love her
And we're a matching pair.

Charley Hodges (10)

My Best Friend Emily

My best friend Emily cheers me up when I'm down
She's as funny as a circus clown
Emily is cuter than 1000 kittens
Gentle and warm like my fluffy yellow mittens

As smart as my English teacher
Quieter than a tiny sly creature
More colourful than a parrot
Healthier than a carrot

Emily makes time fly
She smells delicious like homemade apple pie
Her eyes blue like the deep sea
Her hair shiny and soft like a pop star's on TV.

Bethany Wilson (9)

My Favourite Person

My favourite person is my mum
she makes me smile when I feel glum
Mum comforts me when I'm feeling sad
and shares my joy when I am glad

I help Mum with things I can
like making my bed or feeding the cat
So then we can share some leisure time
doing fun things like swimming or flying a kite

Mum cooks for me my favourite food
that is pasta, salad and chicken too
We enjoy watching films and videos
or going to town to buy new shoes.

Libby Spokes (10)

Me And My Dog

I love my dog called Sophie,
She is my special one,
She's always pleased to see me
And we both have lots of fun.

If I'm feeling very sad,
She will come and cuddle me,
And then I feel much better,
She is the best friend there could be.

She will always be my favourite friend,
No matter what she does,
I know that I can count on her
When things are sometimes rough.

Chloe Mead (9)

My Reason For Writing, My Inspiration

My favourite person is J K Rowling
My reason for writing, my inspiration,
With incredible thoughts
And powerful dreams,
She has what I want,
And had what I have.
Now, so I dream,
Think, write and scribble,
In hope that my worlds
Can be shared with you.
My dream is contained in this one little wish
Because she is my reason for writing this.

Holly Riglar (15)

My Brother Hash

My brother is the best
even though he's a pest.
His nickname's Hash
he's always throwing trash.
He's two years old
and his head is very bald.
He loves eating but
he's very good at cheating.
He loves his baked beans
makes a big mess of his jeans.
My brother may be a pest
but he will always be the best.

Maryam Shafiq (10)

My Favourite Person

You are always there for me,
In the morning,
In the evening,
You're reliable, understanding and fun.

All these things make my favourite person
And maybe you are but,
Who it is, is a mystery,
Fun, enjoyable, sensitive,
Polite, funny and kind.

Now I have included everything about my favourite person,
It is your turn to guess who it is!

Hanisha Kaur (12)

My BFFL Tilly (My Dog)

Tilly totty
Silly Tilly
Wagging all day
Tickle her tummy
She'll be your buddy

Fun, cute, full of excitement
She has a teddy that she adores
Standing on her hind legs
We have to applaud

My little Tilly, she's three
And boy does she enjoy her cup of tea.

Brittany Buttle (10)

Number 1 Mum

This is the woman who got to the final of Pop Idol,
The idol of my heart,
The faith who guides me through rough times.

This is the person who makes immaculate food,
Her pasta fills me up, not with food but with joy
And gives me a good year every year.

This is the one who says a soulful, 'Goodnight,' every night,
Her voice is sweet and perfect in every way,
The ultimate number 1 Mum
      This is . . .
      My mum Gela Best.

Saffron-Alicia Best (9)

My Friend Guy!

M y friend Guy is cool!
Y es but mad!

F rightened of wasps? Definitely
R eally he is
I always give him half of my lunch when he forgets his
E very time I go to his, we play in the fields
N aughty but funny!
D oes have another friend called William.

G uy is cool and that's how he is
U nderstanding sometimes
Y es, that's him, he's great!

Jake Coombs (10)

My Favourite Person

My favourite person is . . .
My mum because she . . .
Cooks for me
Cleans for me
Helps me
And is a great artist!

Invites my friends round for me
Books a holiday for me
Is a taxi for me
And looks after me!

That's why my mum is my favourite person!

Rebekah Smith (10)

My Favourite Person . . . Otto

Otto, my little black puppy
Makes me smile and be extra happy.

He's black as the night
And stands out on white,
Otto, my little cute puppy.

He makes me laugh when he plays,
He is hilarious some days.

He runs like a cheetah
And after drinks a whole litre.

Otto, my little funny puppy.

Sammy Fowler (9)

My Dad

My dad rides a fast bicycle
He's as cool as an icicle

My dad's a great bodyboarder
He likes to keep the waves in order

My dad likes to rock out
Play it loud and scream and shout

My dad's got a collection of Hot Wheels
That he got on eBay deals

My dad likes to play guitar
But sometimes thinks he's a rock star!

Jessica Apps (10)

Snorkmadian

His name is Snorkmadian,
He is pitch-black and shiny silver.

He has a thin double tail that swishes from side to side,
As he swims round his hexagonal tank.

His bulgy eyes sit on either side of his mouth,
Like a hammerhead shark.

His scales shimmer like shiny pebbles in the light of the sun,
Bubbles of all sizes come out of his mouth,
In fact, it is probably big enough to be a tunnel for a miniature train.

He is a blackmoore goldfish!

Emily Millard (9)

My Sister Bethany

She makes me smile, she makes me laugh
But most of all she's my sister
She looks down on me
However I will always look up to her.
The best thing of all she helps me get through
The lonely and scary times.

Although we bicker we will always love one another
So as time passes on we will continue to look out for each other.
My sister and me, when we get in from school
We give each other a smile
And think what a wonderful sister we have.

Danielle Thornborough (11)

My Big Sister

My big sister is the best
and very different from the rest.
She taught me how to crawl
and helps me when I fall.

My big sister.

She always hugs me when I'm sad
and looks after me when I feel bad.
She taught me lots of maths
and how not to be afraid of cats.

My one and only big sister.

Emily Cribb (10)

My Favourite Person

My favourite person
Is very special to me
And is as busy as a bee.
She is kind and loving too,
She always thinks of you,
She brightens up the day,
She is caring in every way,
She is always there to bring a smile,
Every day and all the while,
There are those who think she is yum,
But to me she is *my mum.*

Georgia Middleton (10)

My Favourite Person In 2009

My favourite person is not only a baby!
My favourite person is a smart baby.
My favourite person laughs at all my jokes,
Even if I'm not funny.
My favourite person talks to me
More than anyone.
My favourite person plays with me.
My favourite person cries
When I go to school or leave him.
My favourite person is
My baby brother, Jorge.

Luana Ebiogwu (11)

My Favourite Person Is My Dad

When I'm feeling down and sad
I know I can go and talk to my dad.
He knows so much,
How to cheer me up,
My dad is my favourite person.
As we sit on a chair,
For me he's always there
Because he really cares.
I love my dad, he's always in my heart,
Forever.

Natalie Warner (11)

My Superior Sister

My older sister is superior to me,
She was there for me when I could not see,
I look up to her and all the successful things she has done,
She shines so bright just like the sun,
She is very funny and full of life,
But always comes to my sandwich and takes a bite,
All the good times we've spent together,
No matter what the weather,
That is why I am glad to call her . . .
My superior sister.

Yassmine Akesbi (11)

My Favourite Person

She loves her earrings hoopy,
Her laugh is kinda loopy,
But I love her gorgeous smile,
And her black straightened hair goes on for miles,
She's an angel come from Heaven,
She'll be there for me forever,
I love her with all my heart,
I ache when we're apart,
So my big sister Jai is my favourite person,
Cos it's plain to see that she's the best big sis there'll ever be!

Madeeha Anam Rafique (12)

My Favourite Person

My favourite person is Jamie Oliver,
He inspired me to want to be a chef.
I always watch his shows on television.
When he cooks it's like magic.
I can't help myself but I want to cook it as well.
Sometimes after I see recipes that I want to cook,
When my mum is cooking I ask her if I can help
But when she says no I pretend to cook with my Play Doh.
When it comes to cooking Jamie Oliver knows what is healthy eating.
I like cooking, that's why Jamie Oliver is my favourite person.

Panashe Danga (9)

Untitled

That night when they told us the foster child was coming
We were excitedly fussing around running
Then there was a knock at the door
He thought nobody loved him or cared anymore
A few weeks later after he came to stay
He made a friend and started to play
Soon after he had to go
That night I felt so low
Then I heard from him
He was OK, he had settled in.

Rebecca Cliffe (11)

My Cat Hamish

I've got a pussycat called Hamish
and he is very fluffy.
When he sees another cat,
his tail goes all puffy
and when his tail goes puffy,
it is very funny
and when his tail's puffy,
it is very fluffy.
My best friend is my fluffy,
puffy, funny pussycat called Hamish!

Phoebe Nickolls (8)

One, Two, Three, Four, Five, Six And Seven

Michelle my mum gets everything done,
Christopher my dad helps out around,
Jacob my brother is a massive bother,
Elleanor my sister gives me blisters,
Thomas the toddler is a bit of a wanderer,
Pyper the baby plays on my DS game,
But the one that I love the most is,
Of course the remote control!

Megan Chadwick (9)

My Mum's Tests

My mum is just the best,
She could pass any test,
Except cooking chips cos she burns them to bits!

My mum is just the best,
She could pass any test,
Except cooking cos she's the pits!

My mum is just the best,
She could pass any test,
But who cares she can't cook chips, I still love her to bits!

Thomas Evans (10)

Magnificent Mum - Haikus

Magnificent mum
My mum likes to go shopping
She goes every day

She cooks and washes
She loves the colour purple
She watches TV

Mum loves drinking tea
Favourite food is baked beans
Mum hates Brussels sprouts.

Meredith Webb (10)

Chloe

Friends are there when you're down
Friends are there when you're lonely
That's why my best friend is Chloe,

Friends can be nice
Friends can be funny
That's why my best friend is Chloe,

Chloe is an extremely lovely person
That's why we're friends forever
That's what makes her important.

Katie Greenaway (11)

My Very Special Mum

My mummy is so yummy
I love her so much,
She cares for me and I care about her,
I love her so much, she is magnificent.
Just when I look at her she makes me smile.
I am sorry about being naughty
But I am happy about being good.
I love her so much.
My mum is so nice to be with.

Caitlin Hinds (8)

The Dad I Love And Always Will

I love my dad, he's great
He takes us on outings and gives us pop
(Although Mum doesn't allow it)
He's a great lad
He sings songs (constantly) and gives us treats
He's not really that bad
Actually he is quite sweet
I love my dad
He is a great lad.

Charis Fage (10)

It's Dad

My favourite person
is my dad.
He's sometimes funny
and I'm glad.
He's number 1,
better than Mum.
It's Dad!

Shannon Drew (12)

My Favourite Person

My favourite person is Petter Solberg.
He drives a Subaru which is blue,
He is really, really, really cool.
I watch him rally on the telly,
He drives really fast and makes lots of dust
And sometimes has a little crash.
When I'm a big boy, I want to be like him
And drive a rally car so I can win.
He is the best rally driver in the world.

Liam Griffiths (6)

My Big Bro

My big bro is my favourite person in the world
because he is like my best friend,
because he is someone that I can talk to, no matter what,
if I need cheering up, he is there,
if I need someone to play with, he is there,
but most of all when I need someone to hug and love,
he will be there,
that is why my big bro is my favourite person
in the whole wide world.

Troy Crombie (12)

My Parents

P eople who look after me
A lways make me smile
R eally help me
E verything they do is good
N ever let me go
T rusting in me
S ometimes they are superstars.

Lewis Hunter (8)

My Favourite Person

My favourite people are simply my parents
The ones who look after me
One time I fell, they picked me up
And kissed my little grazed knee
They comforted me and made me
Smile though it hurt for a little while
They put on a plaster and a little cream
And from that moment I knew that
My parents loved me.

Lena Jones (10)

Granda Joe

My favourite person is Granda Joe
He loves to walk in the snow
He loves to walk
He loves to talk
I love my granda Joe
He loves rabbits
He loves birds
He loves dogs
But most of all he loves me!

Alicia Reid (11)

Monday Morning

Monday morning an angel goes to work,
Her beautiful hair as red as a blazing fire,
Gracefully she dances round the house,
Carefully she washes her beautiful crystals,
Her beautiful white fluffy wings start to flutter,
She knows it's time to teach the other angels how to fly.
The angel is my mum, the one who inspires me!

Kes Sinfield (10)

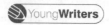

He Taught Me

He taught me to love
He taught me to care.
How to feel free
And how to share.
He taught me respect,
He taught me creation,
To always be myself,
He is my inspiration . . .
For he taught me well.

Lancy Miranda (14)

My Grandad

My favourite person has to be
The one thing that always helps me,
Whether I'm good or bad,
Happy or sad,
It has to be my grandad,
All the time we spend together,
We will be there for each other,
All the times we help one another
Makes our friendship even better.

Jaymie Wright (10)

All About Adam

Adam is my favourite friend.
We always play with each other,
Every time I play with him I feel like he's my brother.
We go to school together but we don't sit together
But we will be best friends forever no matter what the weather,
Adam's always kind to me, my best friend,
Adam forever.

Lisa-Marie Curley (8)

My Favourite Person

I have a dog called Zara, she is my favourite pet
She was not well the other day, so we took her to the vet's
The vet gave her an injection and a large pill
If we had not taken her, she would have been very ill
As days went by she slept and ate
She would eat everything we put on her plate
By the end of the week, she was herself again
She was running, playing and barking again
I'm glad Zara's better because she's my best friend.

Georgia Watts (9)

Debs

She's small, but cool
And her favourite colour's blue.
She loves a hot bath and chocolates too,
She works very hard to get me what I want,
But what she wants for me is to do well at school.
I have no brothers or sisters, just one, that's me!
But when my favourite person comes home,
She's all I need,
Just my mum and me.

Indiana Fofie-Collins (9)

My Mum

My favourite person is:
The best person she can be,
Loves me even through the rough times,
Looks after my guinea pig with me,
She tells me I look beautiful,
Even when I'm grumpy,
This person is my mum.

Joanna Poole (11)

My Favourite Person

My idol,
The person I look up to,
Orlando Bloom.

We share two things in common,
He is an actor and I dream to be,
We both have dyslexia.

That is why, he is my idol,
My favourite person.

Harry Siderfin (9)

My Favourite People

My favourite people are different you see,
They're not like you, they're not like me.
They're small and fluffy with nice long tails,
To make me happy they never fail.

My gerbils are funny, they're cute too!
We've got so many, their cage is a zoo.
They watch the computer, they watch the TV,
They sit on the sofa just beside me!

Siobhan Lock (10)

Bobbie-Lee

Your brown eyes and big fluffy ears,
You bring me joyful tears,
You can gallop, canter, trot and walk
And did you know, I wish you could talk?
If you did, I wonder what you would say,
'Hey, Jamielee, can you get me some hay?'
Before I bring my poem to its end,
My love for you I want to send.

Jamielee Zwart (10)

Brother Harry

He is a darling boy.
He laughs, he giggles and really is a joy.
When I come in the room he always smiles and laughs.
He even has a giggle when he's in the bubble bath.

I read him stories and tell him all of the things we will do,
Of ships and boats and sailing trips, to which he replies, 'Coo.'
I love my baby brother, he really is tiptop
And even I giggle when his bottom does a pop.

Chloë Ball (8)

My Rabbit Pablo

Pablo is a rabbit, his face is soft and cute,
He bites a lot and eats a lot and his volume is at mute.
When we got him from Rushden his ears were down and unhappy,
But when he was at home with us his eyes lit up and he was happy.

When we took him on a walk he burrowed by all the trees,
We took him to the allotments and he nearly ate all the peas!
When we put him in his hutch he wanted to go to sleep,
So we walked off and then suddenly we heard him counting sheep!

Henry Dearn

My Mum Is A Treat

When I look at the sun I think of my mum,
Warm and sunny, she's very funny.
Laughing and smiling, no care in the land,
That's how I feel when I'm holding her hand.

When things go wrong, she's always strong,
Kind, caring, loving and sharing.
My mum's the best sweet in the shop,
My mum's a treat, like a lollipop.

Kayley Sharp (11)

Blankey!

B ubbly and bouncy
L oving and little
A lways on outings
N ever a pest
K ind and caring
E ager and easy
Y es I'll take him . . .

. . . and that's *Blankey!*

Sarah Warner (10)

My Mum

Early in the morning, I think of you,
Nearly every minute, you are on my mind.
I fear the day you might forget me,
I shed tears at being left behind.

You are as sweet as a pear,
As tough as a bear,
My love for you will never tear,
Like steel it will wear and wear.

Georgia Howard (9)

Jacqueline Wilson

'Secrets', 'Bad Girls'
are some books that she has written,
'The Lottie Project', 'The Cat Mummy',
the one about the kitten.

Jacqueline Wilson's who I'm talking about,
my favourite writer.
The stories she's written like 'Lola Rose',
couldn't be any brighter.

Kirstie Goodchild (9)

My Favourite Person

Becca is my cousin, her real name is Rebecca.
She loves me with all her heart,
Which is the size of a double-decker!
She has always been there for me since the day I was born,
She is beautiful, sweet and kind
And her hair colour's just like corn.
She is really nice, sweet and kind,
And she is the best person you'll ever find!

Amy Ingram (9)

My Favourite Person In The World

My favourite person in the world is my mom
She's always there, she always listens
She gives me courage to be strong
Nobody understands quite like Mom
She loves me and cares for me all the time
We spend loads of time together
Nearly every second of every day together
That's why my mom is my favourite person in the world.

Aston Crombie (10)

My Nanna

My nanna is the best in the whole wide world
She always has biscuits and crisps
She will always cook you what you want
I love my nanna to bits
My nanna gives the best cuddles
She is always there for me too
Thanks for being my nanna
I love you!

Harvey Bolton (9)

My Best Friend

My mum is not just my mum,
She is my best friend.
A friend that I will always need,
A friend is what we need.
My mum is not just my best friend,
She means everything to me.
She is my world,
And that's why I am me.

Chanttel Wright (10)

Deborah

Deborah is my best friend
And always will be till the end
She is always there for me
Through trouble, thick and thin
We always sit together
And we will always be together
That is why Deborah is my favourite person of 2009
Debbie is mine!

Amy Crain (11)

My Mum

My favourite person is my mum,
Making yummy food for my tum.
Telling me wrong from right,
Holding my hand tight.
She always knows how to make me smile,
Won't let me be sad, even for a while.
Looking after me night and day,
In each other's hearts we will always stay.

Gurneet Brar (10)

My Friend Alex!

She and I have a great time,
Laughing about meaningless things!
She and I have lots of fun,
Prancing like well-posh kings!
I'd like her to know,
She's my very best mate!
And I'd like to be friends
Till we're ninety-eight!

Beth Egan (12)

My Beloved Grandma

I like my grandma, she is so good
She does everything a grandma should
She has a beautiful smile on her face
And she also makes some gorgeous cakes
But one day it went bad
Everyone was so sad
She finally passed away
And I am still sad till this very day.

Mustafa Elsherkisi (11)

Me And My Dog

Me and my dog have loads of fun
Especially when we have races to run
Me and my dog play lots of ball games
Football, catch and tennis in the lane
My dog is Cindy and I am Jade
When we're together we are never afraid
So you see, my special person is my four-legged friend
And we will be together until the very end.

Jade Viccars (10)

My Mum

Everyone has a favourite person,
So do I,
It's not my teachers, nor my favourite basketball player,
It is my mum,
Who is as hard and strong as a rock,
To make us smile she goes through a lot,
Her smile makes every pain go away,
She has always been special and my favourite person.

Nabeeda Bakali (13)

My Baby Brother

He roars like a tiger which always makes me laugh.
He looks funny when he dances and also likes his baths
With his big brown eyes and his long curly eyelashes
He's always smiling and is as cute as can be.
His favourite teddy is Blue Bear with its soft fluffy hair.
He plays with him all the time, always taking care.
He may have a lot of wind which makes him go ooh.
He's my beautiful brother even if he's from the zoo.

Rebecca Jeffery (8)

Flavia's My Hero!

Flavia's my hero in every way,
She can dance with a sway, a sway, a sway!
Her feet can dance at the dead of night,
Until it becomes so very bright.
My dream is for her to be my friend,
Because we'll take the lead.
Flavia's my hero in every way,
She can dance with a . . . sway, a sway, a sway!

Jessica Francis (10)

Lady GaGa

Lady GaGa is a woman with blonde, bright hair,
I like the way she dances, which gives her flair.
She dresses crazy but I don't seem to care
Because her clothes are as wacky as her hair.
She makes me smile when she sings
With her rhythmical beat
'Cause Lady GaGa is the best
And don't forget what I just said.

Aaliyah Chileshe (11)

My Cats

I have two favourite cats
They are tortoiseshell
And have four legs.

They sleep on my bed
And purr when I stroke them!

They are my best friends
Milly and Moggy.

Arron Drummond (8)

My Favourite Person

My favourite person is my favourite gran
She loves me very much and I love her all the same

One of the things I like about her is she's very kind
I enjoy to be with her all of the time

When I go to her house I love to give her hugs
And I like to help her all of the time
So all that's left to be said is that I love her very much.

Charlotte Hamilton (11)

The Joy Dad Brings

My dad bought me a swimming pool
He makes me happy all the time
He took me fishing
I caught four fish, he caught three
He's letting us and the rest of the family go to America
He's taken me on some trips
I'm sure he's going to take me on some more.

Samuel Lewis Lunn (8)

My Mum

She cooks for me
She cleans for me and she's my hero.
Unfortunately she won't be around forever.
She's a wonder,
She means the world to me.
Someday I wish to be like her,
She's my mum.

Tiaylor-Marie Davis (8)

My Friend, Jess

Jess is my best friend
We play ponies and horses
Nothing can stop us
Just running around
We don't make a sound
We play on the mound
Together.

Charlotte Cooper (9)

My Auntie

My auntie lives one hundred miles away
In a place called Nuneaton
She makes me feel happy
When I am sad
She is a very special auntie
So I just want to say
Auntie, I love you in every single way.

Lauren Emily Cadge (12)

My Dad

My dad is the best,
My dad is the worst,
My dad is the strongest in the world,
My mum is lucky to have a great husband,
My dad is the best
In the *world!*

Bethani Partridge (11)

My Favourite Person

Me and my mother, we love each other
And we also help out one another.
Me and my mother stick up for each other
And play with each other, including my brother.
My mother loves me
And I love my mother!

Sam Cooper (9)

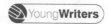

My Mum

Someone who cares and someone who loves me,
Someone who listens and someone who's funny,
Someone that helps me through hard situations and
Someone that helps me make brand new creations.
She's cool, she's crazy, she's fab and she's fun,
What more could I ask from my mum?

Erin Fyfe-McWilliam (11)

My Mummy

My mummy has long brown hair,
When I need her, she's always there,
Her deep blue eyes just stare.

My mummy is a great cook,
Lovely holidays she does book,
She stuns you with her beautiful looks.

My mummy loves me a lot,
She buys flowers for her flower pot,
She likes the weather when it's hot.

I love my mummy lots and lots!

Emily Moore (10)

All About Lauren

She is cute and she's one year old
She has big blue eyes
She is always smiling
She has pretty clothes and new shoes
I love her lots
Cos she is my little sister.

Jordan Drummond (6)

My Favourite Person

M agic teacher who is so kind
I ntelligent, never seems to mind
S ensible and fair, always there
S uccessful, creative all through the year

O lympic medals are given as rewards, tempting us and making us care
L ovely ways, keeping up our best
I ncredible, friendly, wanting us to learn
V ery happy with her smile so bright
E nthusiastic, encouraging and calm
R eading, writing, maths and science have been such fun
   involving us all - she's my number one.

Ben Morgan (9)

Grandad Allan

My grandad Allan is very kind,
He never has a bad thought in mind.
We go to our favourite places,
We sometimes walk 100 paces.
He is always there for me,
We have good times, me and he.

Cameron Cook (10)

My Favourite Person

I know I love her
I love her vey much
She does not need a finishing touch
She is like the stars above
I know she is the one who I love
She is my *mummy!*

Hannah Furness (9)

My Favourite Person, My Grandma!

My grandma is my special friend I hold very dear
Who offers understanding, care and comfort, year by year
A grandma is someone special with a warm and tender touch
That makes the memories shared with her all mean so very much
Who always takes an interest in everything I do
I love my dear old grandma and I hope you love yours too!

Caryn Pearce (11)

My Best Friend

Jack I have to say is my ultimate mate
Whenever I see him he makes me feel great
He always makes a smile appear on my face
We're true good friends in the human race
There's really nothing better than a brill friend
And now this poem has reached the end.

Sam Harvey (10)

My Kitten

She is furry and fluffy and a feline friend
I love to play with her, she is very exciting
So weeny and teeny I love her so much
In a fluffy, feline way
She is my little lucky lady
And the perfect feline friend.

Jade Poyser (8)

Emily And I

Emily and I, we stay side by side,
No matter what catches our eyes,
We won't leave each other's sight.
Whether it's a walk in the park,
Or a fight and she barks,
Our relationship will stay,
And grow stronger every day.
So whatever we go through,
Whatever we see,
I love Emily and she loves me.

It might not be that every day is right,
Once in a while we could have a fight,
But we have lots of adventurous fun,
And lots more still to come.
So whatever wacky adventure,
Or possibility,
I love Emily and she loves me.

In my dreams
Emily always gleams,
Since we met,
She was my favourite pet.

Eleanor Shanahan (10)

My Best Friend

Hollie is my best friend from school,
I love her cos she's really cool.
Skipping is a game we play,
We laugh and dance and sing all day.
We go to each other's house for tea,
Cos I love her and she loves me.

Alicia Ross (6)

Young Writers Information

We hope you have enjoyed reading this
book - and that you will continue to enjoy it
in the coming years.

If you like reading and writing poetry drop us
a line, or give us a call, and we'll send you a
free information pack.

Alternatively if you would like to order further
copies of this book or any of our other titles, then
please give us a call or log onto our website at
www.youngwriters.co.uk

Young Writers Information
Remus House
Coltsfoot Drive
Peterborough
PE2 9JX
(01733) 890066